# The I.Q.
# Obstacle Course

David J. Bodycombe

BARNES
&NOBLE
BOOKS
NEW YORK

*Many thanks to Chris Dickson for his many constructive criticisms of the first draft, suggesting some good puzzles, and helping me "brainstorm" for new ideas.*

*Thanks also go to:*
  *My aunt, Enid McNamara, for her help in making the book "America-friendly."*
  *My friends for their supportive curiosity.*
  *Nick Robinson, Jan Chamier, and Mark Crean at  Robinson Publishing for their backing, scrutiny, and guidance.*
  *My parents, Sheila and David, who have helped with testing ideas or looking up curious information for a long time.*

Originally published as *The Mammoth Book of Brainstorming Puzzles, Round One*

Copyright clipart used in this book originates from the following companies: 3G Graphics Inc., Archive Arts, BBL Typographic, Cartesia Software, Corel Corporation, Image Club Graphics Inc., Management Graphics Ltd., One Mile Up Inc., Studio Piazza Xilo M.C., Techpool Studios Inc., Totem Graphics Inc., TNT Designs.

Book Layout by David J. Bodycombe at *Labyrinth Games* using *CorelDraw!* 5, © Corel Corporation 1994. Crosswords produced with the aid of *Crossword Compiler for Windows*, © Antony Lewis 1993-5.

*Word Island* suggested answers checked against *Chambers English Dictionary*, 1990, edited by Catherine Schwarz *et al*.

This edition published by Barnes & Noble, Inc.,
by arrangement with Carroll & Graf Publishers, Inc.

1997 Barnes & Noble Books

ISBN 0-7607-0492-9

Printed and bound in the United States of America

   98 99 00 01 M 9 8 7 6 5 4 3 2

QF

# WELCOME

Welcome to *I.Q. Obstacle Course*, which will be especially enjoyed by those with a liking for unusual, devious puzzles. But it's not booby traps all the way – there are some traditional puzzles to make you feel at home.

In each Lap there are ten puzzles. These are graded from 1 to 5 stars in difficulty, with 5 being the hardest, although the one-star puzzles are certainly no walkover! The stars also represent the number of points up for grabs, so solving a five-star puzzle correctly will win you a valuable five points towards your "Target to Beat" score. Up to 30 points can be gained in one Lap. No points are lost for incorrect answers. Use the first page of each Lap to record your scores.

So where's the big catch? You only have 90 minutes to attempt the Lap. Yes, this is harsh but just try your best and you'll soon get used to the pace. At first the target scores are set deliberately low so you can afford to experiment with different tactics before things begin to heat up.

As you progress through the book you may find that you get better at the puzzles and that your score rises. Similarly, the "Target To Beat" we set for you to aim at also increases slowly. See if you can keep up the pace! You can chart your progress on a graph we have prepared for you at the end of the book.

The five different categories of puzzles in this book are listed overleaf, together with brief descriptions of the types of puzzle each one encompasses.

## THE CATEGORIES:

 VERBAL – These questions test your ability to handle letters, recall words and form phrases. Vocabulary can play a part in the harder puzzles.

 NUMBER – Anything number-based is permitted here. Some of the harder puzzles might use a little algebra, but common sense may get you further!

 VISUO-SPATIAL – Requires the ability to observe and move objects around in your mind's eye in two and three dimensions.

 TECHNOLOGICAL – These puzzles often ask you to predict how a simple, real-life mechanical model would behave.

 LATERAL THINKING – Sometimes the right answer can be discovered by thinking "sideways". If you see this icon, beware...

See you at the end of Lap 25!

# LAP 1

Time Limit – 90 minutes

For each correctly solved puzzle award
yourself the number of points shown in the
table below. See if you can beat the target.

| | VALUE | SCORE |
|---|---|---|
| 1. CROSS WORDS | 3 | |
| 2. MAKING A MINT | 1 | |
| 3. ELEMENTARY | 4 | |
| 4. PICK-UP JOB | 5 | |
| 5. PICTURE LINK | 2 | |
| 6. ...AND REASON | 1 | |
| 7. INTERSECTIONS | 4 | |
| 8. CANNONBALL RUN | 2 | |
| 9. LETTER LINES | 5 | |
| 10. ALL SQUARE | 3 | |
| TOTAL (max. 30) | | |

## TARGET TO BEAT – 10 points

The simple crossword below has had the letters A, T and two other letters removed from it wherever they occur. Complete the puzzle.

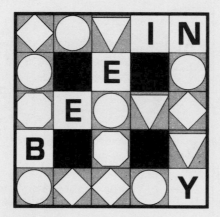

Suppose you have an infinitely large supply of 2p and 5p coins and you wish to buy a packet of mints.

Assuming the shopkeeper doesn't mind the small coins, what is the most the mints could cost given that you are unable to give the shopkeeper the exact money?

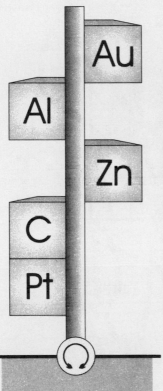

The diagram shows a well-oiled hinge to which five, equal-sized blocks have been attached. The blocks are made from Gold, Aluminium, Zinc, Diamond (carbon), and Platinum.

Bearing in mind the relative weights of these elements, when the hinge is released will it :

A) Swing clockwise?
B) Swing anti-clockwise?
C) Stay vertical?

5

Which word do these letters represent? There is a logical sequence.

**5** PICTURE LINK ★★

What is the common link between the
diagrams shown here?

 **6** ...AND REASON ★

Why might these three words not be very
useful to someone like William Wordsworth?

# MONTH

# ORANGE

# ORIOLE

On the island of Lineus there are four roads which are completely straight. Where any roads cross there is an intersection, and on Lineus there are six intersections (as illustrated). Moreover, no matter how you rearrange the roads one finds that no more than six intersections are required.

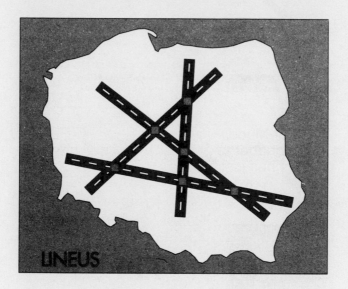

LINEUS

The neighbouring island of Lateralia has fifteen perfectly straight roads. What is the largest possible number of intersections you could expect to see on this isle?

## CANNONBALL RUN
★★

A cannonball is fired and after travelling 5 metres it has reached half its maximum height. After what (horizontal) distance will the shot land? 12m, 18m, 20m, 22m, 28m?

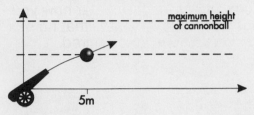

maximum height of cannonball

5m

## LETTER LINES
★★★★★

Professor Muddleup has reordered the letters of the alphabet according to a verbal principle. The Prof has just realized that he has omitted the letter R by accident. Where should he insert it to preserve the logic?

AHBDWEFXLMNS
IJGKQOPCTUVYZ

Here are four miniature pencils, each one of which is two inches long. By moving just one pencil, can you form a square a little bigger than three? (If you find this difficult, look closer at the question.)

# LAP 2

Time Limit – 90 minutes

For each correctly solved puzzle award yourself the number of points shown in the table below. See if you can beat the target.

| | VALUE | SCORE |
|---|---|---|
| 11. GAME FOR A LAUGH | 4 | |
| 12. CANDLE COUNT | 2 | |
| 13. LETTER COGS | 5 | |
| 14. ORDER, ORDER | 3 | |
| 15. ODD MAN OUT | 1 | |
| 16. WORDS APART | 2 | |
| 17. NATIONAL GRID | 5 | |
| 18. SNOOKERED | 3 | |
| 19. LIQUIDATION | 1 | |
| 20. FILL-IN FUN | 4 | |
| TOTAL (max. 30) | | |

## TARGET TO BEAT – 10 points

**11** GAME FOR A LAUGH
★★★★

Although the phrase below sounds like something a hiker might make, the letters can be rearranged to form the names of a piece of sports equipment and two games pieces. What are they? (They are all 6-letter words.)

# THUMBED PROPOSITION

 **12** CANDLE COUNT
★★

Since my birth I have always had a birthday cake, decorated with the appropriate number of candles.

To date, I have extinguished 253 candles in all. How old am I?

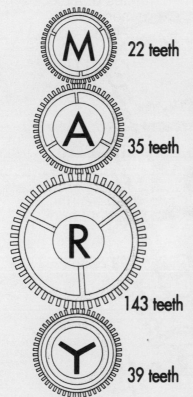

**22 teeth**

**35 teeth**

**143 teeth**

**39 teeth**

The diagram represents four cogs which bear the number of teeth indicated. The letters on the cogs, read downwards, spell the word MARY.

The wheels begin to turn. How many times does the largest (143 toothed) cog have to turn before a four letter word is shown again?

# Which letter should appear in the final disc?

## 15 ODD MAN OUT
★

Which picture doesn't belong?

## 16 WORDS APART
★ ★

Look carefully at the words in the box. Which word on the right could also be put inside the box to preserve the logic?

WEIGHING
MONOPOLY
REDEFINE
AUGUSTUS
ECDEMITE
TOMNODDY
OUTBURST

HANDBOOK

HEREUNTO

HIJACKER

HOBBYIST

HUMANELY

15

In an effort to design a foolproof system against power cuts, the UK National Grid is considering connecting every town directly to every other town with one long power line. The diagram shows that if four towns are connected in this way, six wires are required.

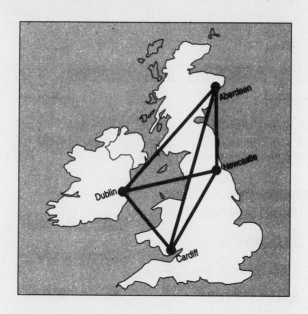

If there are about 895 towns and cities in the UK how many power lines would be required for this mythical scheme to be implemented? Ignore the complications of wires crossing over one another or over the sea.

## 18 SNOOKERED
★ ★ ★

A cue ball is fired around a 5 x 6 foot pool table. The ball is struck from pocket 4 such that the ball moves one foot vertically for every two feet travelled horizontally.

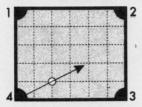

In which pocket will the cue ball end up, assuming it has enough power and the cushions do not affect the expected path of the ball?

## 19 LIQUIDATION
★

A ballbearing is to be dropped into each of these beakers. In which experiment will the ball travel the slowest?

| WATER | MILK | OIL | TAR |
|-------|------|-----|-----|
| at | at | at | at |
| 20°F | 40°F | 60°F | 80°F |

Work out the logic and fill in the missing square.

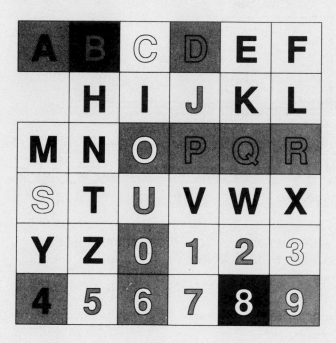

| A | B | C | D | E | F |
|---|---|---|---|---|---|
|   | H | I | J | K | L |
| M | N | O | P | Q | R |
| S | T | U | V | W | X |
| Y | Z | 0 | 1 | 2 | 3 |
| 4 | 5 | 6 | 7 | 8 | 9 |

# LAP 3

Time Limit – 90 minutes

For each correctly solved puzzle award yourself the number of points shown in the table below. See if you can beat the target.

| | VALUE | SCORE |
|---|---|---|
| 21. ROPE AND CHAIN | 5 | |
| 22. TRIANGLE TEASER | 3 | |
| 23. GLASS EYE | 1 | |
| 24. DIAL 'M' FOR MYSTERY | 4 | |
| 25. ROUTES | 2 | |
| 26. DECAP | 3 | |
| 27. PAT. PENDING | 1 | |
| 28. SLEEPING SATELLITE | 4 | |
| 29. HANDY RIDDLE | 2 | |
| 30. PIN PICK | 5 | |
| TOTAL (max. 30) | | |

## TARGET TO BEAT – 11 points

19

# 21 ROPE AND CHAIN
★ ★ ★ ★ ★

Place the letters on the rope and chain such that an English word can be read both clockwise and anticlockwise on the chain and the rope, giving four words in all.

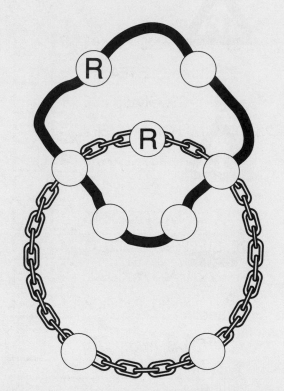

A D E F I P R R S

20

Which number should replace the question mark?

The cross section shown (right) is of a lens.

Will this type of lens help correct the eyesight of short-sighted or long-sighted people?

My friend Jon has a telephone number that I can never quite remember, so I practise "dialling" the number on my calculator to get into the habit. As it happens, his number is 638468.

I dialled on my telephone to ring him last night but a voice at the other end of the line said "Hello, Newtown 692462".

Can you explain these events and tell me what I had done wrong?

Following the arrows at all times, how many different routes are there from A to B?

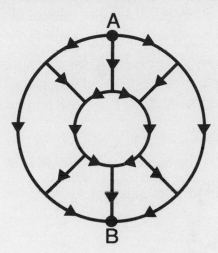

What special change can be made throughout this sentence to make the content rather more pleasant?

"show this bold prussian that praises slaughter, slaughter brings rout"

These two pendulums are just touching. Pendulum A takes 9 seconds to swing to and fro, whilst Pendulum B takes 15 seconds for one cycle.

Assuming the air resistance doesn't slow their motion down, how long would you have to wait to see them touch again?

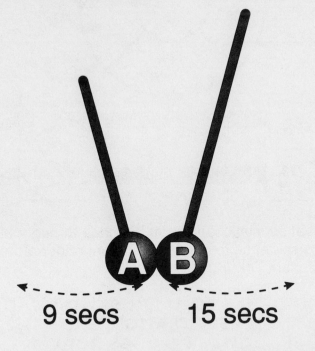

9 secs          15 secs

## 28 SLEEPING SATELLITE
★★★★

Scientists are concerned because in the future there may not be enough room in space to continue launching geostationary satellites. Why is the space so limited for such things?

## 29 HANDY RIDDLE
★★

Can you work out this riddle?

*"When I am filled,*
*I can point the way.*
*When I am empty,*
*Nothing moves me.*
*I have two skins,*
*One without, one within."*

Which pin is the seventh to be picked up in order?

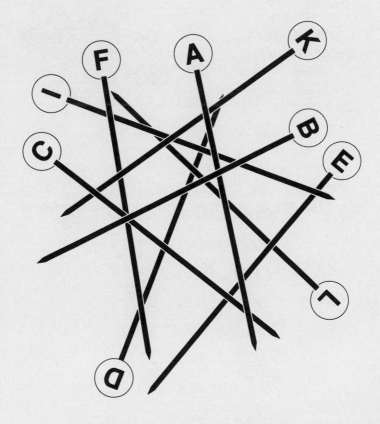

# LAP 4

Time Limit – 90 minutes

For each correctly solved puzzle award yourself the number of points shown in the table below. See if you can beat the target.

| | VALUE | SCORE |
|---|---|---|
| 31. WORD INLETS | 1 | |
| 32. FIGURE IT OUT | 4 | |
| 33. SYNTAX ERROR | 2 | |
| 34. MISSING LINES | 5 | |
| 35. CHESS WORDS | 3 | |
| 36. INITIALLY SPEAKING | 4 | |
| 37. DIAMONDS ARE... | 2 | |
| 38. MEASURE FOR MEASURE | 5 | |
| 39. A TALL STOREY | 3 | |
| 40. POOL POSER | 1 | |
| TOTAL (max. 30) | | |

## TARGET TO BEAT – 11 points

## 31 WORD INLETS "A"
★

Rearrange the same six letters to form words that fit the blanks in the story.

"Charles would _____ some of his friends to go carol singing, carrying _____-covered Christmas garlands. People would _____ as they sang '_____ Night' "

## 32 FIGURE IT OUT
★ ★ ★ ★

Five consecutive numbers have been hidden in the shaded boxes at random.

The numbers within the triangle total 27.
The numbers within the circle total 39.
The numbers within the square total 24.
All five numbers total 65.

In order, what are the five numbers in the diagram?

You may have heard the lateral thinking puzzle about the circus performer weighing 79kg trying to carry three 10kg gold rings across a long bridge that can support 100kg in weight.

The suggested answer found in most puzzle books is that the performer should juggle the rings across the bridge. This is not a good idea, according to which principle of physics?

## MISSING LINES
★★★★★

Complete the last equation with one of the words at the bottom.

**SOAP = RISE**
**FLAY = CLOTH**
**CHAP = BURN**
**MANY = CAT**
**POOP = ?**

**STRING   DECK   PALINDROME   MESS   NEEDY**

## 35   CHESS WORDS
★★★

Can you find the four 11-letter words hidden in the chess board?

Prefix ten letters to spell out a word.

*- CLEF*

*- SPY*

*- STRING*

*- BOAT*

*- MONTHS*

*- BOMB*

*- JUNCTION*

*- BEAM*

*- NECK*

*- LAYER*

## 37 DIAMONDS ARE...
★ ★

How many diamonds, in total, are featured on the cards Ace, 2, 3, ..., 9 and 10 of Diamonds in a standard pack of cards?

## 38 MEASURE FOR MEASURE
★ ★ ★ ★ ★

The bottle shown is sealed but is partly filled with liquid.

Using only a standard ruler, how could you mathematically calculate the volume of the bottle without opening it or damaging it?

There have been many successful aircraft, such as the Boeing 747 and Concorde, which have gone on to set records for speed, reliability, size and length of journeys.

However, aeronautics has, so far, been unable to develop one sort of aircraft so that it can fly a distance greater than 2 miles despite considerable research. What class of aircraft is this?

How many balls are missing from this pool triangle, would you say?

# LAP 5

Time Limit – 90 minutes

For each correctly solved puzzle award yourself the number of points shown in the table below. See if you can beat the target.

| | VALUE | SCORE |
|---|---|---|
| 41. FOUR WORDS | 2 | |
| 42. PRIME TIME | 5 | |
| 43. IDLING ABOUT | 3 | |
| 44. TIMELY MISTAKE | 1 | |
| 45. SQUARE SEQUENCE | 4 | |
| 46. COMPILATION | 5 | |
| 47. MULTIPLYING NUMBERS | 3 | |
| 48. EGGSAMINATION | 1 | |
| 49. DOUBLE PUZZLE | 4 | |
| 50. WORD NETWORK | 2 | |
| TOTAL (max. 30) | | |

## TARGET TO BEAT – 12 points

Which word on the right can NOT be placed together with the words in the box to preserve the logic?

> **AURORA**
>
> **BUREAU**
>
> **COOKIE**
>
> **IGUANA**
>
> **ORIOLE**

**UNIQUE**

**UNITER**

**UREMIA**

**UTOPIA**

**42** PRIME TIME
★★★★★

There are 362,880 different numbers that use the digits 1 to 9 exactly once, such as the example shown below. Of these, what percentage are prime numbers? Round your answer to the nearest 1%.

*192,654,387*

The diagram below represents the cogs A, B, ..., I, J. Suppose these cogs have 36, 34, ..., 20, 18 teeth respectively.

Cog E rotates at 12 revolutions per minute.

How many times faster is cog J rotating than cog A?

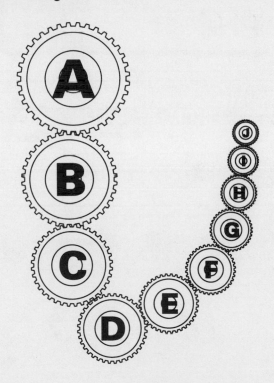

## 44     TIMELY MISTAKE  ·
★

What mistake did this Russian spy make on his forged identity card?

## IDENTITY CARD

Name : Steven Parchell
Address :  2 3 Arch Street,
Helsinki, Finland
D.O.B. : 1 2 / 10 / 46
Sex : Male

## 45     SQUARE SEQUENCE
★ ★ ★ ★

Which of the diagrams on the bottom row continues this sequence?

   1        2        3        4

You'll have done many crosswords in your time, no doubt. Unfortunately I haven't had time to finish compiling this one.

Can you complete this crossword using six valid English words?

Hint – Most of our answers begin with B, L and R; a few more begin with J, N, S and V.

# What number should come next in this series?

You have challenged your friend to an egg spinning contest. Whoever has the egg that keeps spinning the longest will win.

Your friend wins by a considerable margin. What should you check to ensure fair play has taken place?

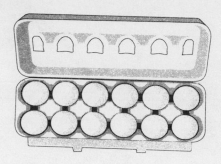

**49** DOUBLE PUZZLE ★★★★

*How many letters are there in the correct answer to this question?*

# WORK NETWORK

★ ★

Spell out an eight-letter word, travelling along each line once only.

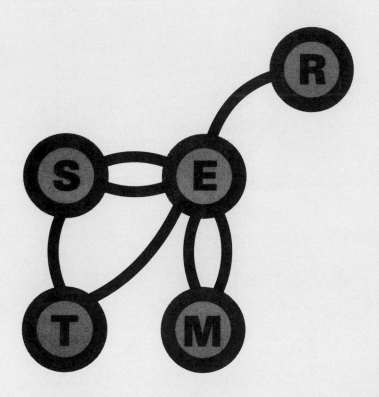

# LAP 6

Time Limit – 90 minutes

For each correctly solved puzzle award yourself the number of points shown in the table below. See if you can beat the target.

| | VALUE | SCORE |
|---|---|---|
| 51. SERIES SOLUTION | 3 | |
| 52. EVEN THIS ONE OUT | 1 | |
| 53. FERRAL ATTRACTION | 4 | |
| 54. WORD CIRCLE | 2 | |
| 55. IN BLACK & WHITE | 5 | |
| 56. CODE BREAKER | 1 | |
| 57. PYTHAGORAS REVISITED | 4 | |
| 58. BALLOON BEHAVIOUR | 2 | |
| 59. DRY DOCK | 5 | |
| 60. SPOT THE SLIP | 3 | |
| TOTAL (max. 30) | | |

## TARGET TO BEAT – 12 points

43

Suggest a word that could correctly continue this sequence :

**AID**
**GUESS**
**DEGREE**
**ESTATE**
**AVENUE**
**SENSE**
**?**

Put 10 crosses in this grid such that there is an even number of crosses in every row and column, and in both main diagonals.

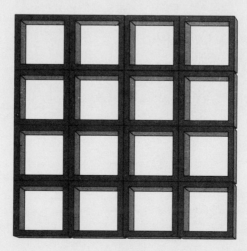

One of these pieces of iron is a bar magnet.
The other one is an unmagnetised iron bar.

Without using any other objects at all, how can
you tell which is which?

What are the LONGEST words that can be read in these words circles?

What word is this?

Using the clues provided, crack the code to reveal the answer.

1. Teacher
2. Printed bill
3. Fancy talk
4. Ticket-entry machine
5. Catholic minister
6. Adheres

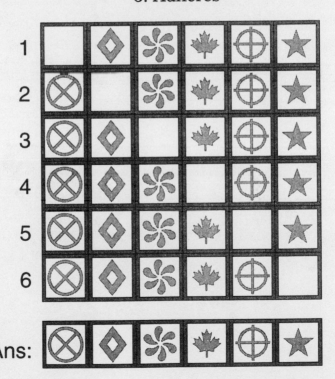

Ans:

## 57 PYTHAGORAS REVISITED
★ ★ ★ ★

Is it possible to construct a triangle like the one shown below such that there is one right angle, two sides are the same, and *a* and *b* are whole numbers?

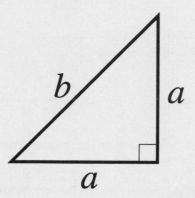

## 58 BALLOON BEHAVIOUR
★ ★

A child is holding the string of an inflated helium balloon in a car which has all its windows shut. When the car goes around a sharp corner, will the balloon :

    a) move into the corner?
    b) move away from the corner?
    c) stay still?

Lying in a well-known sea there is a ship that is worth many millions of pounds. The valuable ship completed its long haul to the destination but it was not able to make the return journey.

So the ship languishes there to this day and, although everyone knows where it is, no attempt has, as yet, been made to recover it.

What is the name of this ship?

## Which of these diagrams is incorrect and why?

# LAP 7

Time Limit – 90 minutes

For each correctly solved puzzle award yourself the number of points shown in the table below. See if you can beat the target.

| | VALUE | SCORE |
|---|---|---|
| 61. ONE WORDS | 4 | |
| 62. BORROW 1, CARRY 1 | 2 | |
| 63. TOSS FOR IT | 5 | |
| 64. PARASCENDING | 3 | |
| 65. SPOT THE SLIP | 1 | |
| 66. SIX ALL | 2 | |
| 67. COLUMNADE | 5 | |
| 68. PEN AND INK | 3 | |
| 69. WITH/WITHOUT | 1 | |
| 70. SQUAREA | 4 | |
| TOTAL (max. 30) | | |

TARGET TO BEAT – 13 points

## What links these pictures?

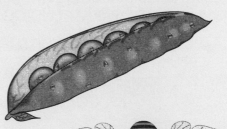

## 62 BORROW 1, CARRY 1
★★

Albert, Bernard and Claire have to share 23, £1 coins in pocket money between them so that:

i) Albert gets half of the total,
ii) Bernard gets a third and
iii) Claire receives an eighth.

"That's impossible to do with these coins," said Albert. "Not if Daddy lends us something," said Claire.

What did their father lend the children, and how much did they each receive?

## 63 TOSS FOR IT
★★★★★

This coin is not made of a uniformly dense metal. Five times out of every six it comes up heads, the rest being tails.

How is it possible to use the coin (as is) to give a fair 50-50 result?

James had just jumped out of an aircraft at 5000ft above hard ground when he looked up and saw a relatively large hole in his parachute. He did not use his reserve chute, no one else was around to help him, and yet he landed safely.

How come he survived?

## 65    SPOT THE SLIP
★

Which picture is incorrect and why?

## 66    SIX ALL
★ ★

What is so special about these six letter words?

**ANIMAL
RECAPS**
    
**SPOONS**
    
**REPAID
DRAWER**

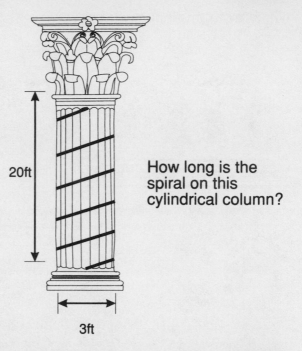

20ft

How long is the
spiral on this
cylindrical column?

3ft

I am trying to write with my ball point pen but
sometimes it works and sometimes it doesn't.
Obviously the way I am using it is having an
effect.

What am I most probably doing wrong?

The items above the line possess a certain property. The items below the line do not. What is the property?

57

What is the area of the shaded square?

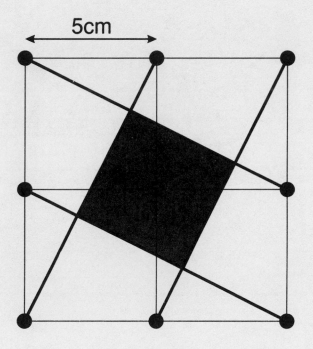

5cm

# LAP 8

Time Limit – 90 minutes

For each correctly solved puzzle award yourself the number of points shown in the table below. See if you can beat the target.

| | VALUE | SCORE |
|---|---|---|
| 71. WHAT'S THE WORD | 5 | |
| 72. RANDOM NUMBERS | 3 | |
| 73. STEEL WHEELS | 1 | |
| 74. HOLEY, HOLEY | 4 | |
| 75. DIVIDE AND CONQUER | 2 | |
| 76. GET IN SHAPE | 3 | |
| 77. DRINK DEBTS | 1 | |
| 78. PULLEY-OVERS | 4 | |
| 79. WITH/WITHOUT | 2 | |
| 80. ROUTES | 5 | |
| TOTAL (max. 30) | | |

## TARGET TO BEAT – 13 points

59

## WHAT'S THE WORD

★ ★ ★ ★ ★

What is the 12-letter word?

Forwards it is :
    Rug; man; mother; B note; calorie

Backwards it is :
    Plant resin; neutral pronoun; living;
    what?; Scottish hat

## RANDOM NUMBERS

★ ★ ★

The letters from 'a' to 'y' are randomly
allocated the values 1 to 25 (a bit like algebra).

On average, what would be the result of the
product :

$$(a-n)\times(b-n)\times(c-n)\times...\times(x-n)\times(y-n)?$$

In which direction will the big wheel turn if the wheel on the right is turning continually in an anticlockwise direction?

## 74  HOLEY, HOLEY
★ ★ ★ ★

There are several very good reasons for designing manhole covers to be round.

Name three.

## 75  DIVIDE AND CONQUER
★ ★

Split the shape below into identically shaped pieces such that each shape contains one of the dots.

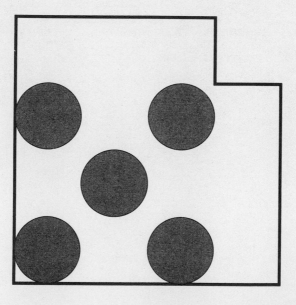

## Which letter should replace the question mark?

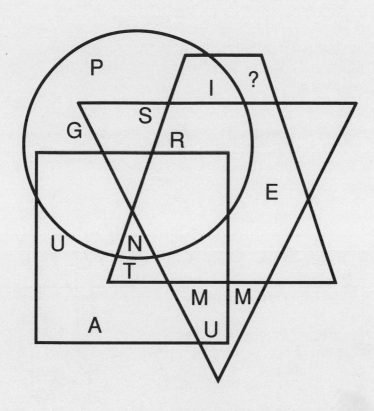

## 77    DRINK DEBTS

★

Four people are in a bar.
Wilf owes Xavier a drink.
Xavier owes Yves two drinks.
Yves owes Zillah three drinks.
Zillah owes Wilf four drinks.

To settle these debts, what is the minimum number of drinks that need to be bought by who for whom?

## 78    PULLEY-OVERS

★ ★ ★ ★

Which of the following statements is/are correct? (Ignore only the weight of the pulleys)

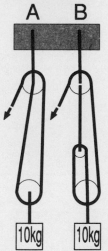

1. Pulleys A and B are equivalent.
2. B's smallest wheel is redundant.
3. B requires less work to be done to raise the weight compared to A.
4. A requires more effort to be put in over a longer distance of rope.
5. A is more energy efficient.

The items above the line possess a certain property. The items below it do not. What is the property?

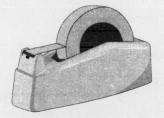

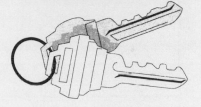

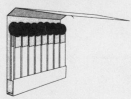

Following the arrows at all times, how many different routes are there from A to B?

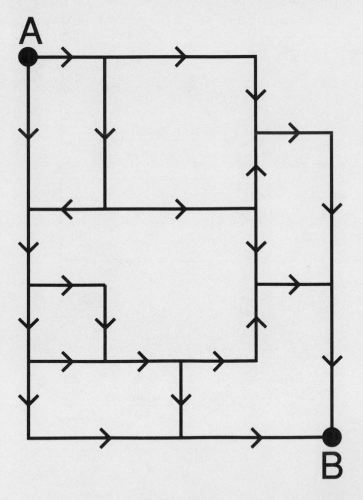

# LAP 9

Time Limit – 90 minutes

For each correctly solved puzzle award yourself the number of points shown in the table below. See if you can beat the target.

| | VALUE | SCORE |
|---|---|---|
| 81. NUMEROLOGY | 1 | |
| 82. CHIP COUNT | 4 | |
| 83. TRIPOD TABLE | 2 | |
| 84. THE FINAL WORD | 5 | |
| 85. POINT-TO-POINT | 3 | |
| 86. TRIGRAPHS | 4 | |
| 87. FOUR PLAY | 2 | |
| 88. IN THE SWING | 5 | |
| 89. MURDER MYSTERY | 3 | |
| 90. NEWSPAPER NUMBERS | 1 | |
| TOTAL (max. 30) | | |

## TARGET TO BEAT – 14 points

Arrange these in order :

LIVES    SEAS

DAY    WISE
CLOCK    MEN

COMMANDMENTS

SENSES    PACK

POSTER    NIGHT
BED    STAND

TIMING

## 82    CHIP COUNT
★ ★ ★ ★

At a certain Nevada casino, gamblers use $5 and $7 chips. What is the largest bet that cannot be placed using these?

## 83    TRIPOD TABLE
★ ★

A tripod for a camera is to be made such that on rugged terrain the feet can be adjusted to make the camera level with the horizontal. How many feet (one, two or all three) need to be made adjustable for this to work?

# THE FINAL WORD

★ ★ ★ ★ ★

Complete the last line with a three letter word.

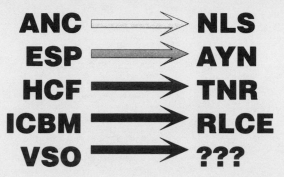

ANC ⟹ NLS

ESP ⟹ AYN

HCF ⟹ TNR

ICBM ⟹ RLCE

VSO ⟹ ???

# POINT-TO-POINT

★ ★ ★

What location can be read here?

Can you complete the dashes to make five English words? Clues to these words (in no particular order) are : baby, flower, Monday?, failure, indicator.

_ _ L T D _ _ _

_ _ G N P _ _ _

_ _ X G L _ _ _

_ _ F S P _ _ _ _

_ _ E K D _ _

## 87 FOUR PLAY
★ ★

What number satisfies the following condition?

"The same result is obtained regardless of whether the number is multiplied by four, or it has four added to it."

## 88 IN THE SWING
★ ★ ★ ★ ★

Ignoring the effects of air resistance, when will both sets of pendulums next touch simultaneously?

The pendulums take the times indicated to swing back and forth.

6 secs.      7 secs.

8 secs.      9 secs.

A man lies dead in a pool of blood and water. Upon inspecting the sorry scene one policeman suggests "It must have been murder and the perpetrator has taken the weapon with him."

A constable doubts this idea very much. "The door was locked from the inside, there are no windows or other ways out of the room, and there are no objects in the room. I suspect suicide. Moreover, I think I know how he did it."

What does the constable think happened?

My newspaper, which has a special 16-page feature in the middle today, is incomplete. The third page of the supplement (page 15 of the newspaper) is missing. What other pages must also be absent?

# LAP 10

Time Limit – 90 minutes

For each correctly solved puzzle award yourself the number of points shown in the table below. See if you can beat the target.

|  | VALUE | SCORE |
| --- | --- | --- |
| 91. WORLD WORDS | 2 | |
| 92. POST HASTE | 5 | |
| 93. TYRING | 3 | |
| 94. FORGETFUL = FATAL | 1 | |
| 95. CIRCULAR ARCH | 4 | |
| 96. SOUNDS FAMILIAR | 5 | |
| 97. CALCULATOR CONFUSION | 3 | |
| 98. BRIGHT SPARK | 1 | |
| 99. AT THE STROKE OF... | 4 | |
| 100. SPOT THE SLIP | 2 | |
| TOTAL (max. 30) | | |

## TARGET TO BEAT – 14 points

What diagram fits in the final space? As is often the case, there is a clue in the title.

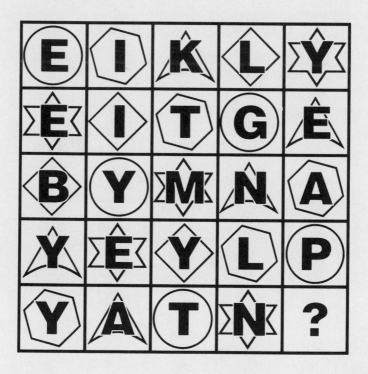

## 92     POST HASTE
★ ★ ★ ★ ★

Postie Pete has a square letter measuring 28cm by 28cm which does not bend. The letter is for the Robinson household but no-one is in to collect the packet, and the only hole in the locked door is 21cm wide. The hole is wider than it is tall.

How did Postie Pete push the letter through the door?

## 93     TYRING
★ ★ ★

Given that the radii of the circles in the dIagram are 1, 2, 3, 4 and 5 units, which statement is true for this tyre?

The tyre's cross-section (in black) is :

(i) larger than
(ii) the same as
(iii) smaller than

the cross-section of the hub (shaded).

A lifeboat arrives on the scene of a catastrophe in the Pacific Ocean, about five miles off the coast of California.

A deserted yacht is surrounded by several dead bodies floating in the sea. What did someone forget to do?

The bottom of the ladder is exactly in the middle of a tunnel. The floor of the tunnel is ten metres wide. Can you tell us how long the ladder is?

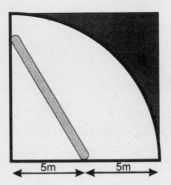

5m       5m

## 96    SOUNDS FAMILIAR
★ ★ ★ ★ ★

What have the following words got in common?

**BOW**

**DOE**

**RUFF**

**THREW**

## 97 CALCULATOR CONFUSION
### ★ ★ ★

When I tap the following keys

into my calculator, the display shows :

I would expect this because :

12 + (one quarter of 12) = 12 + 3 = 15.

However, my father's calculator (which he uses for work every day) gives the answer 16. The calculator is functioning correctly and the same calculator is widely available for sale.

What is my father's profession?

A new six cylinder diesel engine is being designed. It will have a 1.2 litre capacity. The average speed of use is 2,000 revolutions per minute. However, the engine can only work at temperatures of up to 500 degrees Celsius.

How many spark plugs would an experienced engineer recommend to be put in the engine?

## 99 AT THE STROKE OF...
★ ★ ★ ★

Add ONE straight line to make the statement correct.

## 20 10 5 = 4.40

Which picture is incorrect and why?

# LAP 11

Time Limit – 90 minutes

For each correctly solved puzzle award yourself the number of points shown in the table below. See if you can beat the target.

| | VALUE | SCORE |
|---|---|---|
| 101. START TO END | 3 | |
| 102. TENNIS TOTAL | 1 | |
| 103. BOX CLEVER | 4 | |
| 104. THE POWER OF TWO | 2 | |
| 105. IN YOUR AREA | 5 | |
| 106. 21 POSSIBLE | 1 | |
| 107. KING ARTHUR'S TABLE | 4 | |
| 108. SPIN THE WHEEL | 2 | |
| 109. FOUR INSTANCE | 5 | |
| 110. KNIGHTMARE PUZZLE | 3 | |
| TOTAL (max. 30) | | |

TARGET TO BEAT – 15 points

Complete all of the grids to form six common English words.

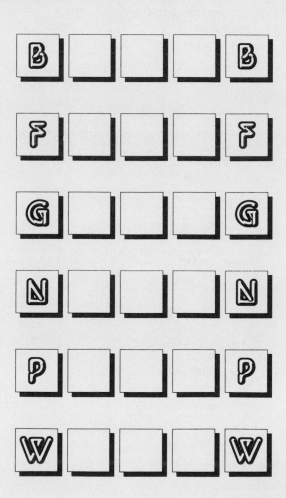

## TENNIS TOTAL
★

What is the least number of points required to win a "Best of three sets" match of tennis (given that your opponent has turned up!)

## 103 BOX CLEVER
★ ★ ★ ★

Which is the odd one out?

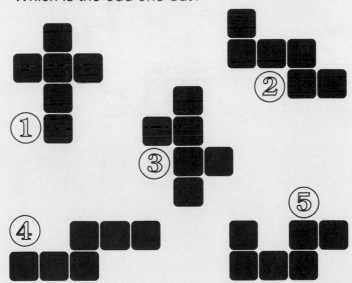

Which three digits replace the question marks at the end of this sequence?

(Hint – try not to think of these as three-figure numbers.)

Here 12 miniature pencils (each 1 inch long) have been used to make a figure which has an area of six square inches. Rearrange the pencils to make a figure which encloses an area of three square inches.

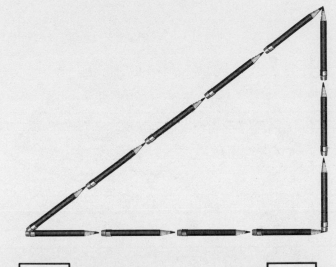

**106** **21 POSSIBLE** "A"
★

What is so special about the following word?

# NYMPHLY

87

**KING ARTHUR'S TABLE**
★ ★ ★ ★

The famous round table is in the corner of a room. It just touches a 5ft by 10ft chest of drawers as shown in the diagram below.

Therefore, how wide is the table?

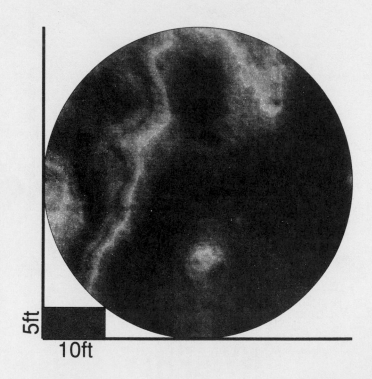

5ft

10ft

Cog A, which has 8 teeth, is rotating clockwise at 27 revolutions per minute. At what speed is cog B rotating if it has 36 teeth?

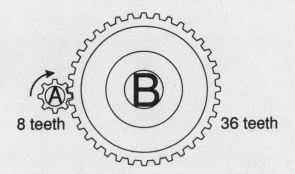

8 teeth        36 teeth

## 109 FOUR INSTANCE
★ ★ ★ ★ ★

Where should Professor Muddleup insert the number four that is currently missing from the line-up?

## KNIGHTMARE PUZZLE
★ ★ ★

Place seven more knights so that all 64
squares are attacked by at least one knight.

# LAP 12

Time Limit – 90 minutes

For each correctly solved puzzle award yourself the number of points shown in the table below. See if you can beat the target.

| | VALUE | SCORE |
|---|---|---|
| 111. TRIGRAPHS | 4 | |
| 112. TRIANGLE TEASER | 2 | |
| 113. WATCH THIS SPACE | 5 | |
| 114. AT LAST | 3 | |
| 115. OBJECTION | 1 | |
| 116. PICTURE LINK | 2 | |
| 117. POOL PERMUTATIONS | 5 | |
| 118. DRIVEN BANDY | 3 | |
| 119. CLOCK-WISE | 1 | |
| 120. NEXT-DOOR NUMBERS | 4 | |
| TOTAL (max. 30) | | |

## TARGET TO BEAT – 15 points

# 111 TRIGRAPHS "A"
★ ★ ★ ★

Complete the dashes to make English words.
Clues to these words (in no particular order)
are : meeting, wood cutter, gossip source,
hold-up, office.

_ K Y J _ _ _

_ _ Z Z S _ _

_ _ _ P E V _ _ _

_ _ _ _ E Z V _ _ _

_ _ A D Q _ _ _ _ _ _

# 112 TRIANGLE TEASER
★ ★

What number should replace the question
mark? Hint – it's simpler than it looks.

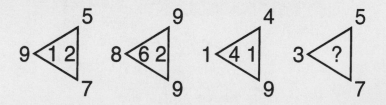

A man gets out of bed and finds himself in a strange place. He takes a coin out of his pocket and spins it on the floor. The coin quickly stops spinning and falls to the ground.

This was enough information to tell the man (a physicist) where he was. Where?

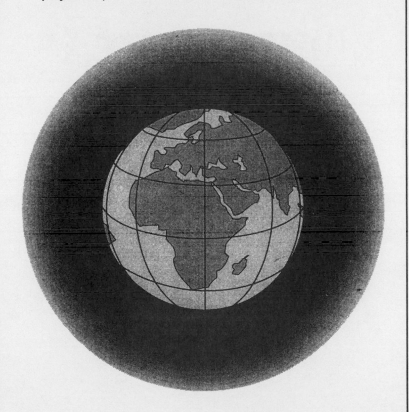

**114** AT LAST
★★★

Which letter should replace the question
mark?

 **115** OBJECTION
★

$$? = 0.5$$
$$N = 11$$
$$D = 100$$
$$X = 6$$
$$Y = 20$$

What famous object or landmark is this?

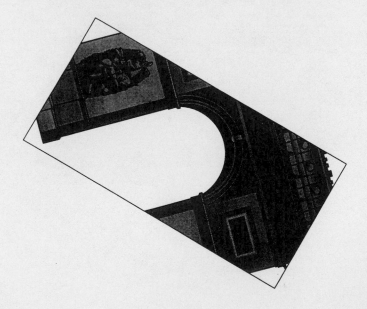

94

Can you work out which four-letter word you could best associate with the following pictures?

The diagram shows a triangle holding 15 pool balls. Seven are yellow, seven are red, and one is black. How many different ways are there of arranging the triangle such that each one is different?

Remember that a triangle can be turned through 120 degrees and look the same.

When the wheel on the left begins to turn clockwise :

    (a) The ball will roll to the left?
    (b) The ball will roll to the right?
    (c) The tray will stay level and go up?
    (d) The tray will stay level and go down?

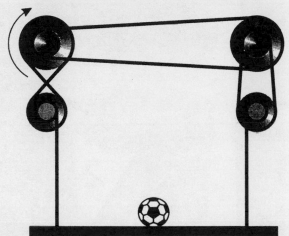

## 119    CLOCK-WISE
★

Despite the fact that there has never been a standard formally laid down, no culture uses a clock that goes in the direction shown on the right. How come?

Which number should replace the question mark to preserve the logic?

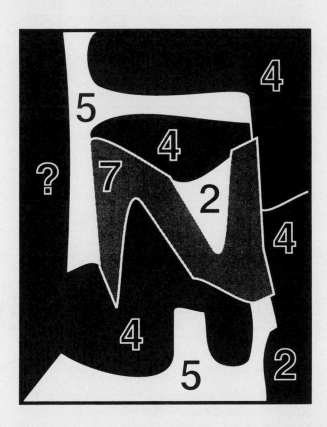

# LAP 13

Time Limit – 90 minutes

For each correctly solved puzzle award yourself the number of points shown in the table below. See if you can beat the target.

| | VALUE | SCORE |
|---|---|---|
| 121. ANY WHICH WAY | 5 | |
| 122. CHECK IT OUT | 3 | |
| 123. BENDY BAND | 1 | |
| 124. WORDY WISE | 4 | |
| 125. RANK AND FILE | 2 | |
| 126. PAIR UP | 3 | |
| 127. THREE OF A KIND | 1 | |
| 128. DI-ABOLICAL | 4 | |
| 129. CRACK AWAY | 2 | |
| 130. DICEDLY DIFFICULT | 5 | |
| TOTAL (max. 30) | | |

## TARGET TO BEAT – 16 points

Which property do the following have in common?

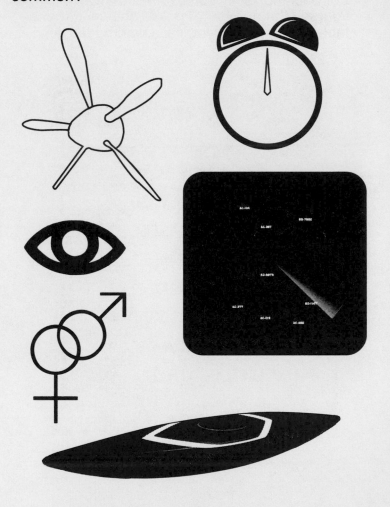

## 122    CHECK IT OUT
### ★ ★ ★

If you bought some CDs (costing a total of £27.80) along with 32 cans of lemonade, 88 postcards and a large amount of 12p sweets, why would you be suspicious if the total cost was £64.78?

## 123    BENDY BAND
### ★

The strip of rectangular paper shown has a half twist put in it such that when the narrow edges are glued together it forms a complete arrow.

How many (a) faces and (b) edges does the resulting construction have?

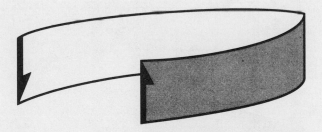

**WORDY WISE**
★★★★

What words are represented below?

ABCDEFGHIJKLM
ABCDEFGHIJKLMNOP

 STUVW

125

**RANK AND FILE**
★★

Add stars, circles and leaves to the grid below such that there is one of each symbol in every row and column.

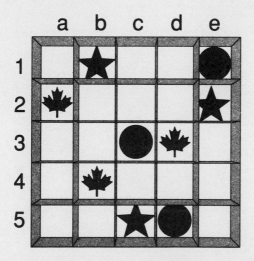

102

Pair these words together :

HOTEL    GLARE

CHUCKLE    RITZ

BREAKFAST

SMOKE    FLAME

GLAMOROUS

SNORT    MOTOR

lunch    FOG

Which number should come next in this sequence?

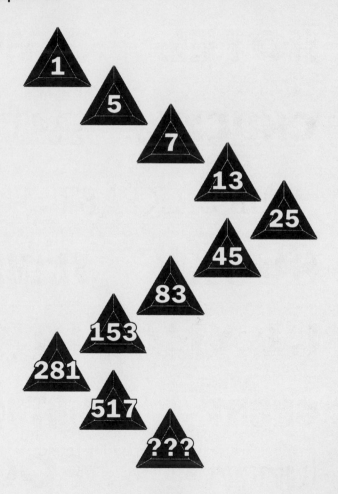

**DI-ABOLICAL**
★ ★ ★ ★

Which die is different from the other three?

1

2

3

4

 **CRACK AWAY**
★ ★

What was the first man-made object to travel faster than Mach 1 (the speed of sound). It is more ancient than you might think...

105

Here are two views of the same cube. Five of the sides have been shown between the two drawings. Draw the hidden sixth side.

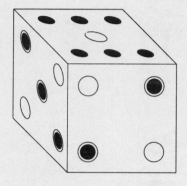

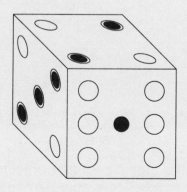

# LAP 14

Time Limit – 90 minutes

For each correctly solved puzzle award yourself the number of points shown in the table below. See if you can beat the target.

| | VALUE | SCORE |
|---|---|---|
| 131. WHERE FOR ART | 1 | |
| 132. ACRE MONEY MAKER | 4 | |
| 133. SYMBOL STATUS | 2 | |
| 134. ANTIPODEAN ARITHMETIC | 5 | |
| 135. SHIP SHAPE | 3 | |
| 136. MISSING PAIRS | 4 | |
| 137. THREE DIRECTIONAL | 2 | |
| 138. AMBIDEXTROUS CLOCKS | 5 | |
| 139. MENTAL METAL | 3 | |
| 140. IN THE MINORITY | 1 | |
| TOTAL (max. 30) | | |

## TARGET TO BEAT – 16 points

Which letter ends this sequence?

# JRUOLMIEEO?

An estate agent is selling four acres of land for £15,000 or seven acres for £24,000. He doesn't mind which offer people choose because he makes the same profit on either deal.

Today he sold 26 acres. How much profit did he make?

What does the following spell out?

## 134 ANTIPODEAN ARITHMETIC
★ ★ ★ ★ ★

By moving just ONE line, change the
subtraction sum such that it is then possible to
read a correct sum.

$$182 - 882 = 695$$

## 135 SHIP SHAPE
★ ★ ★

Ship S patrols an area of coastal waters in
such a way that the distance from lighthouse A
to the ship to lighthouse B is always a total of
10km. What shape does the path of the ship
take?

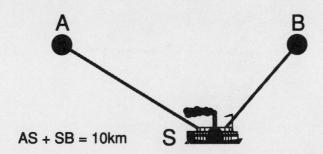

A                                    B

AS + SB = 10km      S

110

Which word below would be allowed into the box without destroying the logic?

**ACERBIC**

**ACRONYM**

**AFFABLE**

**ANTENNA**

**ANXIOUS**

**ASSAULT**

**LIONESS**

**NETWORK**

**FREIGHTER**

**PUNINESS**

What number should replace the question mark?

## 138 AMBIDEXTROUS CLOCKS
★ ★ ★ ★ ★

How many times per day are the hands of a clock "confusable"? For example, clock A could be interpreted as either approx. 3:56 or 11:19, but clock B could only be 5:15 since the hour hand is in the wrong place for it to be seen as 2:37.

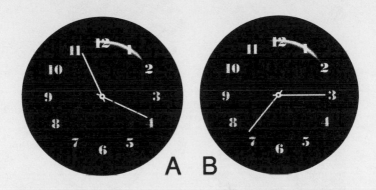

A   B

## 139 MENTAL METAL
★ ★ ★

You have a tank full of mercury, measuring 10 by 10 by 10 centimetres. You also have nine steel ballbearings measuring 3 centimetres across. You drop the balls into the tank one at a time. How many balls will be completely submerged by the mercury?

Which is the odd one out in this group of objects?

# LAP 15

Time Limit – 90 minutes

For each correctly solved puzzle award yourself the number of points shown in the table below. See if you can beat the target.

| | VALUE | SCORE |
|---|---|---|
| 141. ECHOWORDS | 2 | |
| 142. SUM DIGITS | 5 | |
| 143. HOT METAL | 3 | |
| 144. COUNTDOWN | 1 | |
| 145. CUBE COUNT | 4 | |
| 146. NUMBER'S UP | 5 | |
| 147. MANY NINES | 3 | |
| 148. NET RESULT | 1 | |
| 149. ALPHABET ADD-UP | 4 | |
| 150. STAR STRUCK | 2 | |
| TOTAL (max. 30) | | |

## TARGET TO BEAT – 17 points

We want to know what the seven letter word is. The other clues should help you.

Express again

Land

Country

Gallery

Consumed

If you wrote out all the numbers from 1 to 15, the total value of all the DIGITS you used would be :

1 + 2 + 3 + 4 + 5 + 6 + 7 + 8 + 9 +
1+0 + 1+1 + 1+2 + 1+3 + 1+4 + 1+5 = 66.

Can you work out the total of the digits from 1 to 999,999?

Suppose the metallic strip below is heated all over. Which diagram at the bottom of the page best represents the shape of the strip after heating?

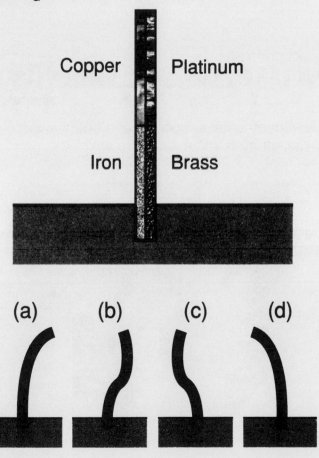

Copper        Platinum

Iron        Brass

(a)        (b)        (c)        (d)

**144** COUNTDOWN ★

Why do the "countdowns" at the beginning of old movies go :

# 10, NINE, 8, 7, SIX, 5, 4, 3?

 **145** CUBE COUNT ★★★★

How many smaller cubes have been visibly removed from this 4 x 4 x 4 cube?

What would come next in this sequence?

1000

1,000,000,000

1,000,000,000,000,000,000,000,000,000,000

100

1

4

8

3

Note – In the UK the first number would be 101 and the third number would be a 1 with 48 zeros after it. The second number might also be different. This information may provide all readers with an extra clue.

**147** MANY NINES ★ ★ ★

Some people think that the recurring decimal 0.99999... (where the dots represent a never-ending row of 9s) is the same thing as 1.

Other people don't agree. They think "No matter how many 9s you add, you'll never quite get to 1 exactly."

Which is right :
      (a) 0.99999... is the same as 1;
      (b) 0.99999... is not the same as 1?

 **148** NET RESULT ★

What object would the following shape resemble when folded up?

What expression from those (a) to (e) at the bottom of the page would suitably complete the final equation?

HOB ✕ IST ＝ Craftsman

UNS ✚ LED ＝ Fallen

NON ✚ SED ＝ Perplexed

AIM ━ LY ＝ Purposeless

MIS ━ NLY ＝ ?

(a) without
(b) with error
(c) withdrawal
(d) winsome
(e) winterwear

121

Which of the four numbered pieces is NOT used in the construction of the completed star-shaped cake-cutter at the bottom of the page?

# LAP 16

Time Limit – 90 minutes

For each correctly solved puzzle award yourself the number of points shown in the table below. See if you can beat the target.

| | VALUE | SCORE |
|---|---|---|
| 151. A FABULOUS WORD | 3 | |
| 152. STEAK YOUR CLAIM | 1 | |
| 153. A BORING QUESTION | 4 | |
| 154. ABLE ALEX | 2 | |
| 155. MIRROR, MIRROR | 5 | |
| 156. TOTALLY USEFUL | 1 | |
| 157. TELEGRAPH TEASER | 4 | |
| 158. BELT UP | 2 | |
| 159. ON THE RIGHT TRACK | 5 | |
| 160. MENTAL BLOCKS | 3 | |
| TOTAL (max. 30) | | |

## TARGET TO BEAT – 17 points

151 A FABULOUS WORD
★★★

Which word is suggested by :

"Midday starting block Last of the Mohicans
second in command bottom of the barrel
second guess at wit's end beginning of the end
starting line early years"?

 152 STEAK YOUR CLAIM
★

Smorgers the Chef has six steaks that each
require 10 minutes of browning on each side.
He only has one pan, which can hold two
steaks at a time.

What is the least
amount of time
required before
all six steaks are
brown on both
sides?

Willy the Woodworm plans to bore through as many wooden cubes as possible (from the 3 by 3 by 3 stack of cubes shown) by starting at one corner and going from cube to adjacent cube, ending in the middle.

What is the largest number of cubes he could possibly chew through?

Alex was once asked a very strange question in his science class :

"Was Noah good at biology?"

He didn't really know the answer, but came up with the right idea after thinking for a little while about what they had been taught last lesson.

What do you think he answered and why?

**155** MIRROR, MIRROR
★ ★ ★ ★ ★

Continue the sequence for the remaining
letters. (The numbers are used for reference in
the solutions.)

| 1 | A | | | | M | | | TUVW |
|---|---|---|---|---|---|---|---|---|
| 2 | BCDE | | | K | | | | |
| 3 | | | | HI | | NO | S | |
| 4 | | | FG | J | L | | PQR | |

 **156** TOTALLY USEFUL
★

What is REALLY special about the following
sentence?

# Foxy nymphs grab
# quick jived waltz.

A new type of indestructible cable has been put around the world to help the supply of communications. Unfortunately, 100 metres too much cable has been made. The engineers decide that it would be best if the cable is propped up by telegraph posts, as shown on the diagram (not to scale).

Approximately, what height would the posts need to be for this crazy idea to work?

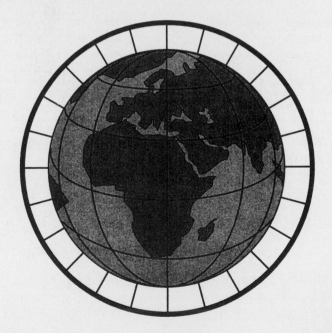

The cog on the right has a clockwise force applied to it. Will the system have an :

(a) odd number of cogs turning clockwise;
(b) even number of cogs turning clockwise?

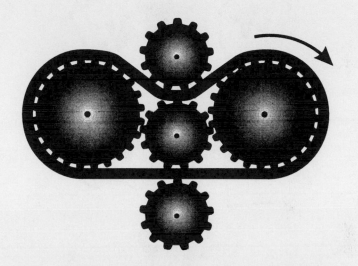

What sort of perfectly ordinary human being would use their right leg to travel 20 metres farther than their left leg on an average day?

# MENTAL BLOCKS
★ ★ ★

What word do these blocks spell out when fitted together? (Guessers beware – there are over 20 different anagrams of these letters!)

130

# LAP 17

Time Limit – 90 minutes

For each correctly solved puzzle award yourself the number of points shown in the table below. See if you can beat the target.

| | VALUE | SCORE |
|---|---|---|
| 161. INITIALLY SPEAKING | 4 | |
| 162. A BAD GAMBLE | 2 | |
| 163. CLOCK ON | 5 | |
| 164. ROMAN RULER? | 3 | |
| 165. PIECE OF PIE | 1 | |
| 166. LIPOGRAM | 2 | |
| 167. SPIRAL SUM | 5 | |
| 168. IN THE SWING | 3 | |
| 169. BRIAN'S BOOB | 1 | |
| 170. SYMBOL SQUARE | 4 | |
| TOTAL (max. 30) | | |

## TARGET TO BEAT – 18 points

What eight-letter word is suggested here?

- **DAY**
- **BOAT**
- **BOMB**
- **SHIRT**
- **BOMB**
- **MOVIE**
- **NUMBERS**
- **RING**

When playing a deadlier version of Russian roulette against an opponent, three bullets are put into consecutive chambers of a six-shooter gun and the barrel is spun.

What is your chance of winning if you have your turn at pulling the trigger first?

132

The readout below is from a 24-hour digital clock. How many times a day will the clock display a "palindromic time"?

(That is, a six digit number which reads the same backwards and forwards, such as 05:22:50 as shown below.)

05:22:50

*"Five hundred begins it, five hundred ends it,*
*Five in the middle is seen.*
*First of all figures, the first of all letters,*
*Take up their stations between.*
*Join all together and then you will bring,*
*Before you the name of an eminent king."*

Which king?

How many circular pieces, each 4 inches wide, can be cut from a pizza that measures 12 inches in diameter?

This is the first sentence from the book *Gadsby*, by E. V. Wright. What is so unusual about it?

*If Youth, throughout all history, had had a champion to stand up for it; to show a doubling world that a child can think; and possibly, do it practically; you wouldn't constantly run across folks today who claim that 'a child don't know anything.'*

The diagram shows a spiral effect constructed with straight lines of increasing length.

So far the length along the whole spiral is 42 centimetres, using twelve lines. Suppose the spiral is extended so that 1000 lines are used. What would the total length of the spiral become?

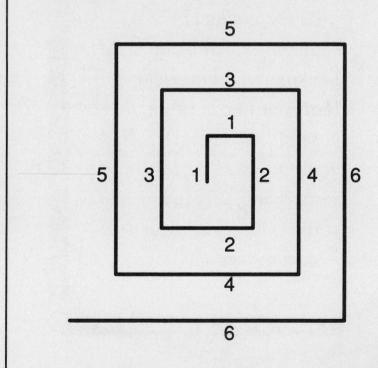

## 168     IN THE SWING
★ ★ ★

At the extremes of their swings, these two pendulums will just touch. Ignoring the effect of air resistance, when will they next touch?

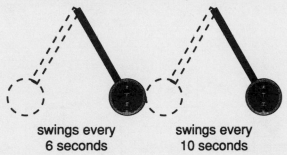

swings every       swings every
6 seconds         10 seconds

## 169     BRIAN'S BOOB
★

Each year on March 27th, my forgetful Uncle Brian has to catch a plane early in the morning from England to go to Saudi Arabia, where he works for half the year. Invariably he misses his flight even though he remembers to turn up at the airport.

Why do you think this happens?

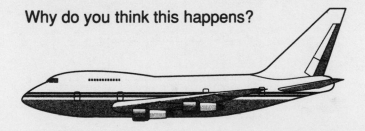

Arrange the tiles into the grid so that the lines read the same across and down (that is, 1 across is the same as 1 down, 2 across is the same as 2 down, etc.)

# LAP 18

Time Limit – 90 minutes

For each correctly solved puzzle award yourself the number of points shown in the table below. See if you can beat the target.

| | VALUE | SCORE |
|---|---|---|
| 171. PICTURE LINK | 5 | |
| 172. TRAIN TRIP | 3 | |
| 173. STEEL WHEELS | 1 | |
| 174. THINK SMALL | 4 | |
| 175. ROTOBALLS | 2 | |
| 176. PART THREE | 3 | |
| 177. GET THE POINT? | 1 | |
| 178. CUBISM | 4 | |
| 179. TWO WOMEN | 2 | |
| 180. CHESS COVER | 5 | |
| TOTAL (max. 30) | | |

## TARGET TO BEAT – 18 points

What especially links the following pictures?

## 172   TRAIN TRIP
★ ★ ★

On a train journey, Barney the Boffin travelled from Birmingham. After a quarter of the journey was over the time was 3:31pm. When there was a third of the trip left to go the time was 4:31pm.

At what time did he arrive at the destination?

## 173   STEEL WHEELS
★

These two ballbearings look the same, and they also weigh the same. However, one is made of a solid metal; the other is made from more dense metal and is hollow inside.

Without using any equipment, what is the easiest way to tell which one is hollow and which is solid?

141

**THINK SMALL**
★ ★ ★ ★

What special property do all these letters of the alphabet have?

# C O P S U V W X Z

 **ROTOBALLS**
★ ★

Two balls lie on either side of a hollow, horizontal cylinder. The diameter of the cylinder is three times the diameter of either ball. Both balls are pushed around the cylinder until they return to their respective starting points.

How many more times will the outer ball turn through 360 degrees compared to the inner ball?

### PART THREE

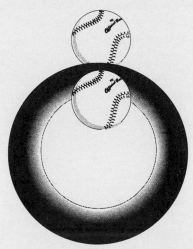

Name eight parts of the body that have three letters in them. There are at least ten.

(They must be proper parts – wax, lap, fat etc. do not count.)

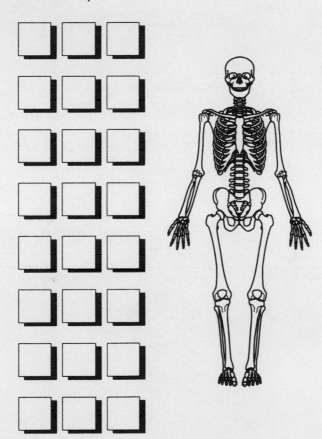

*Which three digit number, when multiplied by 4, is equal to nine?*

Is it possible for the cube on the left to pass through the identical cube on the right if one suitable hole is drilled in the right-hand cube?

There are two women I know :

Deborah was born in 1973 in Cambridge. Katherine was born in the same year, and Cambridge is her town of birth also.

I know that both women have led perfectly normal lifestyles and have normal eyesight and yet I am 99% certain that Katherine has never laid eyes upon Deborah (even unwittingly) and vice versa.

How can I be so sure that this statement is true?

I have one of these chessboards and you have the other. We both have 21 triple dominoes shaped like :

Suppose we both cover our boards with the dominoes. This will cover 63 of the 64 squares on each board. What is the chance that we have the same square uncovered? (And, no, it isn't one in 64.)

# LAP 19

Time Limit – 90 minutes

For each correctly solved puzzle award yourself the number of points shown in the table below. See if you can beat the target.

|  | VALUE | SCORE |
|---|---|---|
| 181. WHAT'S THE WORD? | 1 | |
| 182. POWER PLAY | 4 | |
| 183. MONKEY BUSINESS | 2 | |
| 184. KEEP ON ROCKING | 5 | |
| 185. OUT OF THIS WORLD | 3 | |
| 186. ALL CHANGE | 4 | |
| 187. SYMBOL SUM | 2 | |
| 188. RIGHT ON TIME | 5 | |
| 189. QUESTION = CLUE | 3 | |
| 190. WHAT HAPPENS NEXT? | 1 | |
| TOTAL (max. 30) | | |

TARGET TO BEAT – 18 points

147

## WHAT'S THE WORD?
★

Forwards, this word means "tense".
Backwards, the word means "puddings".

What's the word?

## POWER PLAY
★ ★ ★ ★

This sequence doesn't seem to know whether it should be going up or down. Can you supply the next number?

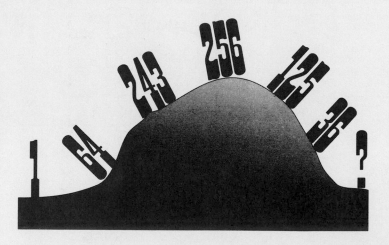

The monkey and the weight each weigh the same amount.

The monkey begins to climb the rope. Will :

(a) the monkey and the weight reach the pulley wheel at the same time;
(b) the weight gets there first;
(c) the monkey gets there first?

Illinois Jones is being chased by a huge 30ft wide boulder – again. The rock is quickly gaining on him and although the tunnel is blocked, he figures out a way to avoid the boulder (just in the nick of time, of course). How does he do it?

**185** OUT OF THIS WORLD
★ ★ ★

What picture should replace the question mark?

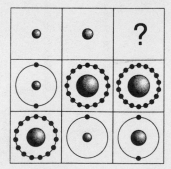

Which one of the words below rightfully belongs inside the box to preserve the logic?

**GOPHER**
**EIGHTH**
**LENGTH**
**WOOFER**
**PREFIX**

**VETOED**

**GRUDGE**

**GIFTED**

**GRUNTS**

**RENNET**

**DIGGER**

**SUNLIT**

**HOGNUT**

Use the numbers and symbols shown to make a correct equation.

$$5 = \times \quad 4$$
$$2 \quad 3 \quad 7 \quad +$$

How many times per day do the hour and minute hands of an analogue clock form a 90 degree (right) angle? One such situation is illustrated.

What number would logically come next in this sequence?

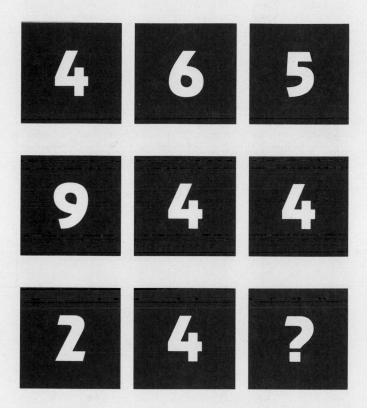

Work out where each square is travelling then use the logic to complete the final picture.

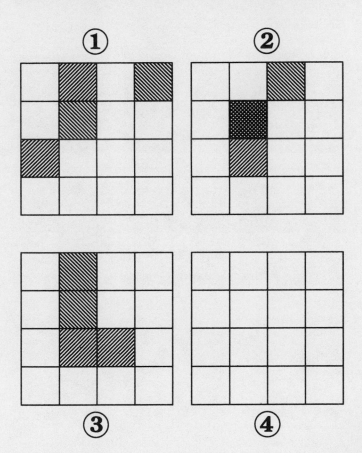

① ② ③ ④

154

Time Limit – 90 minutes

For each correctly solved puzzle award yourself the number of points shown in the table below. See if you can beat the target.

| | VALUE | SCORE |
|---|---|---|
| 191. TIME FOR A... | 2 | |
| 192. SECRET SEVEN | 5 | |
| 193. IN THE PIPELINE | 3 | |
| 194. YOUNG MAN | 1 | |
| 195. DRAW THE LINE | 4 | |
| 196. MISSING... | 5 | |
| 197. APPROACHING ONE | 3 | |
| 198. FULL VOLUME | 1 | |
| 199. TITLED LETTERS | 4 | |
| 200. PLANET POSER | 2 | |
| TOTAL (max. 30) | | |

## TARGET TO BEAT – 19 points

What could be put in the ninth box?

## 192    SECRET SEVEN
★ ★ ★ ★ ★

Imagine that the digit "7" has been banned from use for superstitious reasons. So what we would call "the seventh number" is now written using the symbol "8", the 8th number is "9", the 9th is "10", the 10th is "11", the 16th is "18" and so on.

Complete : The _____th number is written as 4685.

## 193    IN THE PIPELINE
★ ★ ★

Which arrangement of pipes will carry the most water?

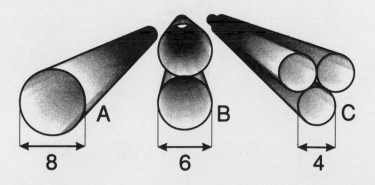

A    8

B    6

C    4

## 194    YOUNG MAN
★

A man was born in the year 1340 and yet he died in the year 1322.

Using the normal calendar, how is this possible?

## 195    DRAW THE LINE
★ ★ ★ ★

Which number replaces the question mark?

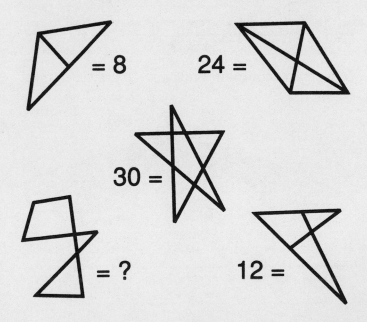

158

**196** ★★★★★

What links the following clues?

O Place in Jordan

O Middle Eastern person

O Libyan leader

O Foreign judge

O Southern hemisphere national airline

O State in Persian Gulf

O Currency of Albania

O Letter of the Hebrew alphabet

**APPROACHING ONE**
★ ★ ★

Which number comes next in this series?

| |
|---|
| 0.5 |

| |
|---|
| 0.6666666 |

| |
|---|
| 0.75 |

| |
|---|
| 0.8 |

| |
|---|
| 0.8333333 |

| |
|---|
| |

## 198 FULL VOLUME
★

Which solid has the most volume? The diagrams are not necessarily to scale.

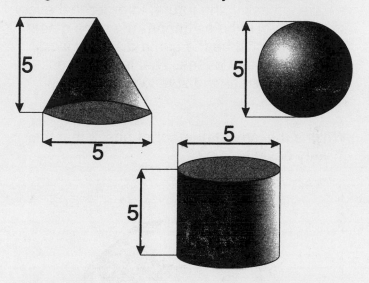

## 199 TITLED LETTERS
★ ★ ★ ★

What is the significance of the following letters?

# MOMMA OFT HOOK BETH
# BORN SIZZLING UPSTREAM

The World Government wishes to place some military bases around Earth to protect against an alien attack in the future. In order that every base is seen to be as important as the others, each base must be the same distance away from all the other bases. That is, any two bases are the same distance apart as any other two bases.

What is the largest number of bases that the military could set up?

# LAP 21

Time Limit – 90 minutes

For each correctly solved puzzle award
yourself the number of points shown in the
table below. See if you can beat the target.

| | VALUE | SCORE |
|---|---|---|
| 201. MIDDLE ROW | 3 | |
| 202. RUN FOR IT | 1 | |
| 203. SIDE-SHOW SCANDAL | 4 | |
| 204. SNAP | 2 | |
| 205. DOMINO DERBY | 5 | |
| 206. LENGTH MATTERS | 1 | |
| 207. NOT NEXT | 4 | |
| 208. GET UP STEAM | 2 | |
| 209. FAME PILLS? | 5 | |
| 210. WORD NETWORK | 3 | |
| TOTAL (max. 30) | | |

## TARGET TO BEAT – 19 points

What is the longest word that can be typed using the middle row keys of a typewriter a maximum of once?

A race over 50 metres results in Vicky beating her twin sister Kris by 10 metres. They decide to have another race, this time with Vicky starting 10 metres behind the start line.

Assuming they run at the same rate as before, who do you think wins now (if anyone)?

"Here's a good trick" said Andrew, offering Sylvia a pack of cards. "Take a card." Sylvia did so and looked at it for a few seconds. "Now put it back into the pack," said Andrew, and Sylvia obliged, putting the card somewhere in the middle of the pack. Andrew squared the pack up well then shuffled it a few times over.

"Now watch," said Andrew. He held the pack in front of Sylvia and as the fingers from his other hand slid up the sides of the pack the card she had chosen emerged straight from the middle of the pack!

Sylvia applauded.
"Great trick," she said,
"how do you do it?"
"Obviously very well!"
said Andrew, "but I will
tell you this – I didn't use
any glue and I didn't
need to know where any
of the cards were in the
pack."

Sylvia couldn't work out
how Andrew rigged his
pack. Can you?

Which of these seven symbols is the odd one out when the other six are correctly paired?

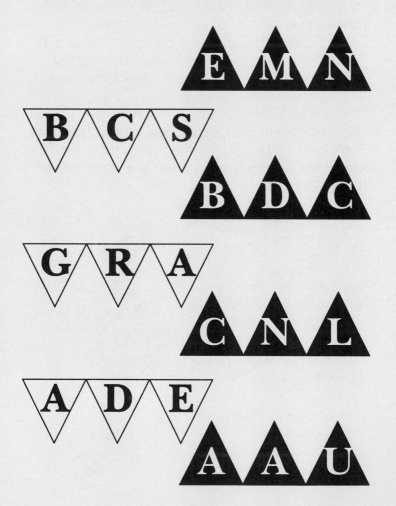

## 205 DOMINO DERBY
★★★★★

Shade out one dot from every domino so that
the numbers of remaining dots in each row,
column and both main diagonals are the same.

## 206 LENGTH MATTERS
★

The longest word that can be read here is...?

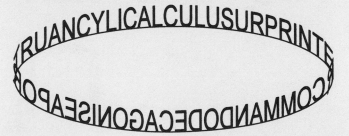

167

Place the numbers 1 through 8 in the boxes below so that no two boxes connected by a straight black line contain consecutive numbers.

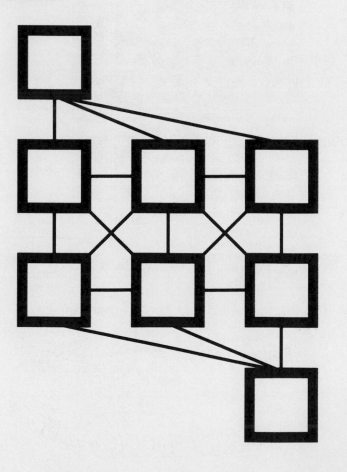

## 208 GET UP STEAM
★★

Professor Muddleup wants to make a refreshing, hot cup of coffee. However, he wants it to remain hot for as long as possible so he wishes to boil his water as long as possible.

Professor Reader (that's you) comes along and sees Muddleup's kettle boiling away. "Just leave that for a few more moments please, I like my coffee really hot," says Muddleup as he munches his break-time biscuits.

What should you point out to him?

## 209 FAME PILLS?
★★★★★

A man takes a couple of tablets. As a result, he becomes famous throughout the world and he will never be forgotten in the foreseeable future.

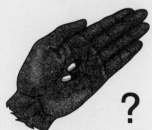

What is his name?

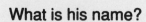

169

Spell out an eleven letter word, travelling along each line once only.

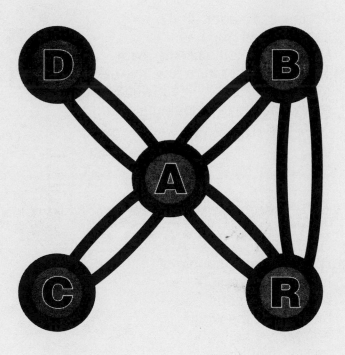

# LAP 22

Time Limit – 90 minutes

For each correctly solved puzzle award yourself the number of points shown in the table below. See if you can beat the target.

| | VALUE | SCORE |
|---|---|---|
| 211. STEP ON UP | 2 | |
| 212. CROSS NUMBER | 5 | |
| 213. START FROM SCRATCH | 3 | |
| 214. CHIRAL BIAS | 1 | |
| 215. DIVIDE & CONQUER | 4 | |
| 216. SWORD WORDS | 5 | |
| 217. SHAPELY SUM | 3 | |
| 218. SPACE PROJECT | 1 | |
| 219. A TYPE OF MURDER | 4 | |
| 220. DRIVEN DOTTY | 2 | |
| TOTAL (max. 30) | | |

## TARGET TO BEAT – 20 points

Complete this crossword to find the unclued word at 10 Across.

### ACROSS

**2** Si, señor (3)
**4** Cloth has a sleep (3)
**6** It tends to mar reputations (4)
**8** Artists use it, if burnt (5)
**10** YOUR ANSWER (6)
**12** Your relation from France? (5)
**13** Made of soap or flour (4)
**14** Cut (3)
**15** Born, sounding like a horse? (3)

### DOWN

**1** Governmental survey (6)
**3** Type of fishy pink? (6)
**5** The people (6)
**7** Make known (6)
**9** Believe, calculate (6)
**11** Get less shallow (6)

172

# 212 — CROSS NUMBER
★ ★ ★ ★ ★

Place nine different digits into the spaces so that six correct equations are formed simultaneously.

|   | + |   | ÷ |   | = | 4 |
|---|---|---|---|---|---|---|
| + |   | + |   | × |   |   |
|   | × |   | − |   | = | 22 |
| + |   | − |   | + |   |   |
|   | × |   | − |   | = | 33 |
| = |   | = |   | = |   |   |
| 11 |   | 3 |   | 19 |   |   |

# 213 — START FROM SCRATCH
★ ★ ★

The tiles below are each scratched by the three rods on the right. How many of the nine possible scratches will there be on the tiles, in total?

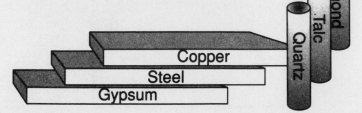

On which side of the line would you place Italy in order to preserve the hidden logic?

| Cyprus | Gibraltar |
| Japan | Argentina |
| India | U.S.A. |
| United Kingdom | Denmark |

Divide this square into sections by drawing two straight lines (which cross at some point in the square) so that the sum of the digits in each section is the same.

6
5   2
  3   8
1
  7

Sword Words are words which form an anagram of another word, such as ARTISTE and TASTIER. Each clue suggests a pair of Sword Words. For each pair, ONE of the two words will fit into the grid below.

When completed, the letters in the arrowed column can themselves be rearranged to make two six-letter Sword Words. What are they?

⬇

1) What the Speaking Clock does?  ☐ M ☐ T

2) Cosy African antelopes  S ☐ U ☐

3) Two fruits  L ☐ ☐ ☐ N

4) Norwegian Spanish man  S ☐ ☐ O ☐

5) Used even more disgraceful language  ☐ ☐ O ☐ E

6) Irregular bullfighters on horseback  ☐ ☐ ☐ R ☐ ☐ I ☐

Clue for final Sword Words :
Crib for a Berlin baby?

☐☐☐☐☐☐
☐☐☐☐☐☐

# SHAPELY SUM
★ ★ ★

Which shape (A, B or C) fits into the grid on the left to make it mathematically correct?

| 11 | 2 |   | 7 |    |
|----|---|---|---|----|
|    |   |   |   | 5  |
| 5  |   |   |   |    |
|    | 7 |   |   | 12 |
| 4  |   | 13|   | 3  |

| 11 | 4  |
|----|----|
|    | 3  | 12 |
|    |    | 1  |
|    |    |    |

A

| 6 | 7  |
|---|----|
|   | 2  | 23 |
|   |    | 4  |
|   |    |    |

B

| 14 | 8 |
|----|---|
|    | 4 | 2 |
|    |   | 5 |

C

## 218

SPACE PROJECT
★

In a national competition children were invited to design experiments to put aboard the next Space Shuttle flight. This attracted much attention in the Science class at Southbury School. One pupil was interested in animal psychology. In particular, she suggested an experiment to observe how birds would respond to weightlessness, by seeing whether they would attempt to fly in their cage.

"I don't think NASA would think much of having dead birds on board!" her teacher said. The pupil could not understand why the teacher was so damning of her experiment – she had made sure in designing it that there would be enough air, water and food for the birds to survive. Can you spot the child's mistake?

The detective entered the room and turned the light on. Jack Steel was found dead, slumped over his computer keyboard. "Looks like Jack's been working too hard for his poor old heart," said the detective. His assistant took a closer look at the screen :

> qnd so I hqve
> decided to tqke my
> life. Pleqse tell my
> zife thqt I love her
> deqrly but I hope
> she understqnds my
> reqsons. There qre
> too mqny auestions.
> ij fghgfff

The assistant beckoned to his superior. "This seems curious for a suicide. Obviously the garbage at the bottom is what he typed when he collapsed on this standard keyboard, but what about the rest?"

"Take a printout," said the detective. "With this evidence we can cut down our enquiries substantially."

What sort of suspects should they look for?

177

Remember how to do dot-to-dot? Trace a path from letter to letter (you will notice that we've already joined up the first word, WHAT). Then tell us what the answer to the riddle is.

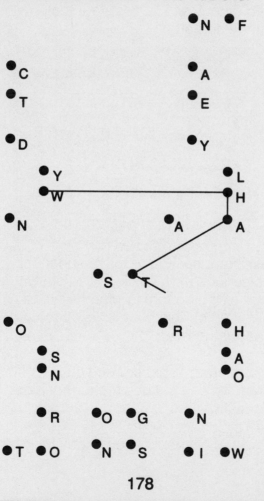

# LAP 23

Time Limit – 90 minutes

For each correctly solved puzzle award yourself the number of points shown in the table below. See if you can beat the target.

| | VALUE | SCORE |
|---|---|---|
| 221. WORDS FROM WORDS | 1 | |
| 222. INPUT, OUTPUT | 4 | |
| 223. CATCH ALL | 2 | |
| 224. ATLAS ADD-UP | 5 | |
| 225. DOMINOES RETURN | 3 | |
| 226. FIRST NINE | 4 | |
| 227. NUMBERS UP | 2 | |
| 228. WORD CUBE | 5 | |
| 229. SEEING RED OVER GREEN | 3 | |
| 230. DIY DOT-TO-DOT | 1 | |
| TOTAL (max. 30) | | |

## TARGET TO BEAT – 20 points

# 221 WORDS FROM WORDS ★

Use the letters of PUZZLE TWO HUNDRED AND TWENTY-ONE once each to form five words. Clues and some letters to start you off are provided.

| Clue | | | | | | |
|---|---|---|---|---|---|---|
| Unit of power | | | T | | | |
| Made into regions | Z | | | | D | |
| Underground passage | | U | | | | L |
| Gentle breeze | | | | H | | R |
| Badly hurt | W | | U | | | |

# 222 INPUT, OUTPUT ★ ★ ★ ★

Several different numbers are put into a computer program which uses a simple formula to determine the number it outputs. Can you tell us what formula the computer is using?

In the three pictures below, a rope is loosely wound around a central pole. When the ends of the rope are pulled away in the direction shown, which picture represents a situation where the rope will catch on the pole?

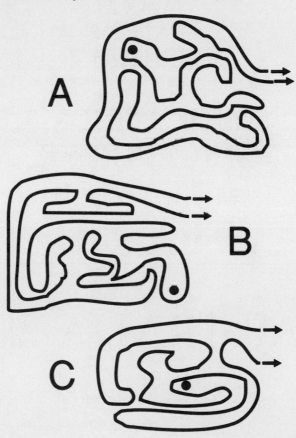

Can you work out the reasoning behind the numbers and thus provide us with the number for Canada?

LIBYA 1
JAPAN 2
FRANCE 3
MAURITIUS 4
JAMAICA 5
SOUTH AFRICA 7
SINGAPORE 8
ICELAND 9
ISRAEL 13
U.K. 17
AUSTRALIA 20
U.S.A. 64

**225** DOMINOES RETURN
★ ★ ★

Place the dominoes in the grid in order to form a total of ten English words across and down.

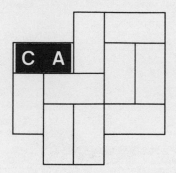

**226** FIRST NINE
★ ★ ★ ★ "A"

I boast that if I take seven of the nine letters below, I can make an English word from them. Can you?

183

What is the last number in this sequence and why?

**100**
**500**
**1**
**50**
**1000**
**5**
**?**

Make up to three twists on this puzzle cube so that it is possible to read two six-letter words. Hint – Don't worry about the orientation of the letters, and the number 9 is a clue.

184

A man stands in the middle of a busy market square on a hot, sunny day. The man takes out a rectangular piece of white cloth from a basket and sets light to it. A few passers-by wonder why he is doing this, but seem unconcerned.

The man then takes out a piece of blue cloth and does the same thing. Again, no one pays very much attention. The man repeats this feat a further six times with red, yellow, black, purple, orange and pink cloths.

Finally, the man takes out a plain green piece of cloth. When he sets it alight, a crowd of distressed onlookers quickly gathers and before long the local police arrive on the scene to arrest him. The man was sentenced in court to a very long jail sentence.

Why did the man get arrested?

Each of the curves in the lower diagram can be placed between a pair of black dots in the upper diagram. Do this for all the lines so that a simple picture is formed.

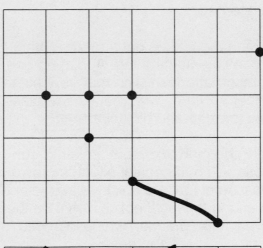

# LAP 24

Time Limit – 90 minutes

For each correctly solved puzzle award yourself the number of points shown in the table below. See if you can beat the target.

| | VALUE | SCORE |
|---|---|---|
| 231. MINI CROSS | 5 | |
| 232. PACK A PUNCH | 3 | |
| 233. CLOCK CURIOSITY | 1 | |
| 234. SYMBOLIC | 4 | |
| 235. BLACKOUT | 2 | |
| 236. LETTER TRACK | 3 | |
| 237. GROOVY | 1 | |
| 238. CUBE VIEW | 4 | |
| 239. POLISH CODE? | 2 | |
| 240. LASER BOUNCE | 5 | |
| TOTAL (max. 30) | | |

## TARGET TO BEAT – 21 points

Solve the miniature cryptic crossword, then rearrange the shaded letters to form your seven-letter answer.

**ACROSS**
1 Branch backs New York baseball team (4)
5 Seasonal variation which turns (4)
6 Green plant in seasonal garden (4)
7 Donna used on the oboe (4)

**DOWN**
1 Celebrity makes rodents turn back (4)
2 Tesselate slab (4)
3 Advantage at the boundary (4)
4 Lady upset alcoholic drink (4)

---

232  PACK A PUNCH
★ ★ ★

In which order would you put these cards on top of one another to form a correct multiplication sum?

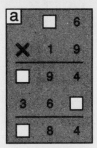
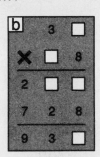
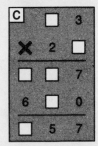

Professor Muddleup was considering an interesting question. He has a large number of modern and antique clocks around the walls of his laboratory. Of these, quite a number of the modern ones do not have numerals on them.

"If that's the case," he wondered, "how am I to know which way up the clock should go? Some of these clocks don't have any marks or other indications that show the user where 12 o'clock is supposed to be."

Tell the Professor why you should never see upside-down clocks, even on models with completely blank faces. (The answer has nothing to do with manufacturer markings on the back of the clock.)

Replace every circle with a number (the same for each circle). Repeat this process with the diamond, and again with the triangle, so that in all you have only used three different numbers. If you have solved the puzzle correctly, the seven rows, columns and diagonal will each add up to the totals indicated.

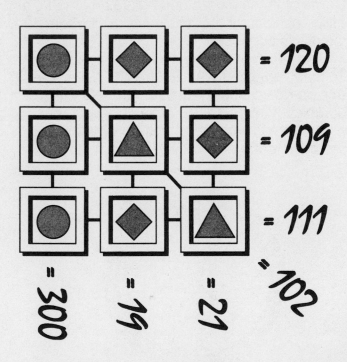

= 120

= 109

= 111

= 102

= 300

= 79

= 27

**BLACKOUT**
★ ★

Shade out eight squares to form four congruent areas (that is, identical in shape and size).

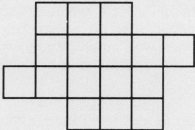

**236**

**LETTER TRACK**
★ ★ ★

Starting from one of the corners, move from square to square to spell out an 11-letter word.

| L | E | R | D |
|---|---|---|---|
| P | H | I | C |
| S | O | N | W |
| U | M | T | A |

Madeleine was playing her long-playing record collection the other day when she came across one of her brother's LPs. She played it and listened to the track, which lasted around four minutes. But then the record finished and the pick-up arm was automatically returned to its holder.

She started the record again in the normal fashion and this time she heard another track! In fact, after playing it many times over the record seemed to play about eight different tracks at random.

How was this possible?

## CUBE VIEW
★ ★ ★ ★

Which two pieces, when welded together, will form a complete 3 x 3 x 3 cube?

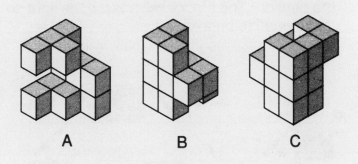

A          B          C

## POLISH CODE?
★ ★

This is a message coded using one of the oldest cryptographic methods known to man. Can you read what it says?

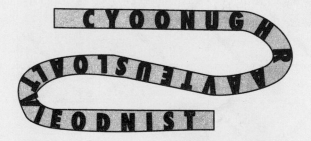

# LASER BOUNCE
★ ★ ★ ★ ★

What is the LEAST number of double-sided mirrors that must be rotated through 90 degrees in order to direct the laser beam to hit the sensor? The blocks will absorb the light so these need to be avoided.

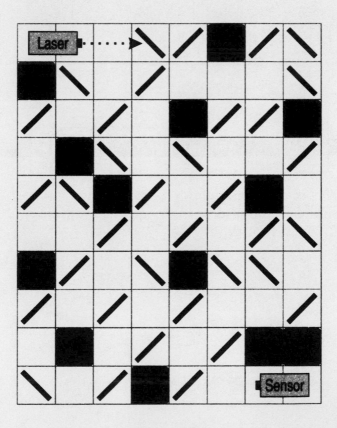

194

# LAP 25

Time Limit – 90 minutes

For each correctly solved puzzle award yourself the number of points shown in the table below. See if you can beat the target.

| | VALUE | SCORE |
|---|---|---|
| 241. CONSONANT CONTENT | 4 | |
| 242. FENCING | 2 | |
| 243. WHERE ON EARTH? | 5 | |
| 244. UNDECIMALIZED | 3 | |
| 245. CUTTING CARD | 1 | |
| 246. EXTRA! !ARTXE | 2 | |
| 247. FIND THEM | 5 | |
| 248. SPRING FOR IT | 3 | |
| 249. ROUND AND ROUND | 1 | |
| 250. PYRAMID COUNT | 4 | |
| TOTAL (max. 30) | | |

## TARGET TO BEAT – 21 points

Put the consonants back into this mini-crossword. The brackets show you the rows from where half of the letters came.

CSX??? {

CLMV???? {

CNY??? {

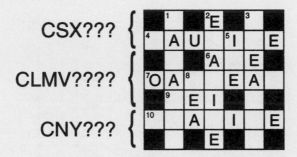

I have some fence posts which I want to use in my garden. Each post is four feet high and between the tops of each pair of posts there hangs a chain.

Each section of chain is six feet long. How close does each pair of fence posts needs to be so that the chain hangs exactly one foot from the ground at its lowest point?

Have you heard this one? "An explorer travels 10 miles south, 10 miles east, then 10 miles north and ends back where he started. Where is his base camp?"

Of course you have, the answer is the North Pole. However, we're not going to ask you the obvious question.

Many puzzle-lovers get the answer to this question partly wrong, or at least, not entirely correct. Although the North Pole is correct, there is also another answer. In fact, an infinite number of answers. We want to know, "Where does there exist an infinite number of points that also satisfy the requirements of this puzzle?"

(In fact, if you think hard enough, there are many, many different answers!)

**244** UNDECIMALIZED
★ ★ ★

In Britain, pounds, shillings and pence were decimalized into our current £s and new pence in 1971. In France, the National Assembly decided upon the metric system of measurement (using decimal figures) in 1791.

However, there was one occasion when there used to be 10 of something which were then "undecimalized" to a larger number, all because of two people. Can you think of the occasion I am referring to?

 **245** CUTTING CARD
★

A quickie – how many squares of 3 x 3 inches (below left) can be cut from the large 22 x 18 inch piece of card (below right)?

**Area = 9 sq. in.**

Area = 396 sq. in.

Sharon had received a telegram from the Queen to congratulate her on reaching her 100th birthday. Sharon's sisters, Marjorie and Norah, are seen in the front-page photo of the local newspaper looking at the telegram.

The next day, Sharon noticed something unusual about the headline. Can you spot it?

**247** FIND THEM
★ ★ ★ ★ ★

Find two DIFFERENT integers that satisfy the following property :

"Take the first number, square it, then subtract the number itself. This gives us a result (let's call it A). Now take the second number and do exactly the same thing, to give us result B. We require A and B to be the same."

Now : list (so far as is possible) EVERY pair of numbers that satisfies this property.

 **248** SPRING FOR IT
★ ★ ★

The left-hand diagrams show how one spring behaves, measured against a ruler. What will be the total distance (marked) AFTER the weight is attached in the right-hand diagram?

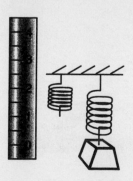

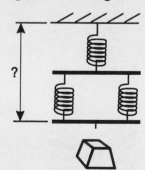

A large group of people board a train. They do so with the full knowledge that they are going to end up at the same place from which they started, and there are no stops along the way. The passengers aren't going to see any rolling landscapes or any local areas of interest.

The passengers have paid money for the trip, but the managers of the train have had very few complaints about the route covered. The train has been running for a number of months but is due to close down soon. It will re-open in the same location next year to follow an identical route.

The train operates many times a day, taking different groups of people each time although a few people sometimes take the journey more than once in the same day.

What sort of train is this?

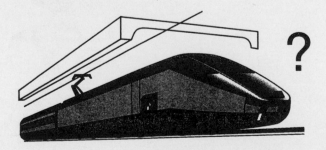

If you added the number of edges this pyramid-based figure has to the number of faces it has, the total you would get is...?

# TOP SECRET

203

1. Across : Satin, Meats, Assay; Down : Samba, Teams, Nasty.

2. 3 pence. Multiples of 2p coins account for even numbered values. One 5p coin and multiples of 2p account for 5p, 7p, 9p, 11p etc. Hence all values above 3p are accounted for.

3. Clockwise. Although the blocks on either side weigh approximately the same, the gold block is further away from the pivot than the other heavy block, the platinum.

4. From back to front, the letters spell out CHEIROMANCY (the art of reading palms).

5. They all have eyes.

6. They do not rhyme with any other words in the English language.

7. 105, since it is the sum $1 + 2 + 3 + ... + 14$.

8. Around 28m. The projectile spends much more time in the upper half of the flight path because the vertical acceleration reduces to zero before the ball starts falling downward.

9. They are ordered alphabetically according to their phonetic sound (ay, aitch, ar, bee, dee, dub'l u, eks, etc.).

10. Move the right-hand pencil over to the left to make a number 4 – which is 2 squared!

11. Bishop (as in chess), Putter, Domino.

12. 22 years, since $1 + 2 + 3 + ... + 22 = 253$.

13. 35 turns to spell WARY. When the largest cog turns one revolution, the other cogs turn a distance of 143 teeth also. The R cog will be upright every 143 teeth, likewise for the A cog every 35 teeth. The M cog displays a letter (M or W) every 11 teeth. The Y cog looks the same every 13 teeth for a similar reason. But "every 11" and "every 13" occurs as a consequence of turning the R cog 143 teeth (since 11 times 13 equals 143). So we need only concern ourselves with the R and the A cogs. Since 35 and 143 are co-prime (that is, they have no common factors: $35 = 7 \times 5$, $143 = 11 \times 13$) then we require 35 turns of the large R cog before the A cog is also in the right place.

14. F, because they represent the places First, Second, Third and Fourth (initial letters).

15. Picture 3; the others are all the same up to rotation. Picture 3 is a reflection of the other pictures.

16. HIJACKER. All the words in the box contain three consecutive letters of the alphabet (eg. eCDEmite, moNOPoly, etc.).

17. 400,065 wires. If there were, say, ten cities, we would need ten more wires to add an eleventh city. Likewise a twelfth city would need eleven more wires, and so on. So the answer we need is the answer to the sum 1 + 2 + ... + 893 + 894. Notice that this is equal to 447 pairs of 895 (look at the first and last number, then the second first and second last number etc. – all these pairs add up to 895). So the answer is 447 x 895 = 400,065.

18. Pocket 2. Remember that the angle the ball makes with the cushion would be identical before and after the rebound.

19. Experiment 1, because water at 20 degrees Fahrenheit is ice!

20. A grey G on a white background. The code used is :
Background colour – white if the letter has no holes in it (like 'M'), grey if it has one (like 'D'), black if it has two (like '8'); Foreground colour – black if the letter is made up of purely straight lines, white if made purely out of curved lines, grey if it is a mixture of straight and curved lines.

21. On the rope – Repaid, Diaper; On the chain – Serif, Fires. Use the E and the I in the intersections.

22. 8, because
    the difference between 2 and 6 is 4
    the difference between 2 and 3 is 1
    the difference between 6 and 3 is 3
The total of these differences is 4 + 1 + 3 = 8.
The same rule applies to all the triangles.

23. Short-sightedness. It is a diverging lens that helps push light rays apart and therefore corrects the over-strong eyeball lens that short-sighted people have.

24. This mystery relies on the fact that calculator and telephone keypads have different layouts, so when I pressed the same pattern of keys on the telephone the numbers were wrong except for the middle row (4, 5, 6).

| 1 | 2 | 3 |
|---|---|---|
| 4 | 5 | 6 |
| 7 | 8 | 9 |

0  Telephone

| 7 | 8 | 9 |
|---|---|---|
| 4 | 5 | 6 |
| 1 | 2 | 3 |

Calculator  0

25. Ten routes.

26. Removing the first letter from each word gives : "How his old russian hat raises laughter, laughter rings out".

27. 45 seconds. A will have swung 5 times, B will have swung 3.

28. All geostationary satellites have to circle around the Earth's equator so that the centripetal acceleration counteracts the radial acceleration. Also, these satellites have to be at a specific height. Therefore there is only really one narrow band of orbits these satellites can take.

29. A glove.

30. The "E" pin. Incidentally, did you notice the pins spell the word BACKFIELD when picked up in order?

31. Enlist, tinsel, listen, Silent.

32. 15, 12, 14, 13, 11 respectively: The numbers are consecutive and add up to 65 so must be 11 to 15 in some order. Using this together with the 1st and 3rd equations (the ones relating to the triangle and square) tells you the number in the circle must be 14. Using the 1st and 4th equation tells you the numbers at the ends add up to 26. Using the first equation we find the number in the square is one less than the second number. Equation 3 says the last two numbers add up to 24, so the first number is two larger than the fourth.

33. By Newton's Third Law of Motion : "Every action has an equal and opposite reaction". In the same way that you feel "heavier" when in a lift going upwards, when a ring is thrown it actually "weighs" more than 10kg's worth of force and the bridge could then give way.

34. NEEDY, because if five lines are added to the words on the left we get SOAR = RISE, FLAX = CLOTH, CHAR = BURN, MANX = CAT and POOR = NEEDY.

35. The black and white letters, when read in a zigzag pattern give : Mountain-top and

Postulation in the top grid, and Contraption and Labradorean in the bottom grid.

36. FIGURATIVE. F-Clef, I-Spy, G-String, U-Boat, A-Bomb, T-Junction, V-Neck are well known. "R-months" are when one is not supposed to eat oysters. An I-Beam is a girder. The E-Layer is part of the atmosphere from which long-range radio waves are reflected.

37. Either 75 or 95, depending on the design of the cards. Each card has either two or four diamonds in the corners which have to be included as well as the main pips.

38. Measure the diameter of the bottom of the bottle. Half it, square it, and multiply by pi to get the surface area of the bottom of the bottle. Measure the height of the liquid and add it to the height of the air when the bottle is turned upside down. Multiply the total with the previously obtained surface area to get the volume of the bottle.

39. Paper aircraft! However, according to the *Guinness Book of Records*, a distance of 1.25 miles has been recorded by throwing a paper airplane from the top floor of a tall building.

40. Five balls, since there are 10 balls present and visual inspection confirms this must be a 15-ball triangle. No estimation is necessary.

41. UNITER, because it only has three vowels whereas all the other words have four.

42. 0%. For all such numbers, the sum of the digits is $1 + 2 + 3 + ... + 9 = 45$, which is $5 \times 9$. This means that the sum of the digits is divisible by 9, and hence (by a well-known mathematical rule) the number itself is divisible by 9. Therefore none of the numbers are prime.

43. Twice as fast. The idlers can be ignored. Since A has twice the number of teeth as J it must be going half as fast.

44. In Scandinavian countries the date is written in the International Date format of YY/MM/DD, so the spy should have put 46/10/12 as his date of birth in order not to arouse suspicion.

45. Picture 1, since the letters A, B, C, D, E, F have been put behind a window.

46. There are 38 words you could use. The most common are bejewel, beveled, beveler, jeweler, jezebel, levered, leverer, leveret, nemeses, receder, redefer, referee, relevel, renewer, reveler, revered, reverer, severer, sewered, venerer.

47. 132, since :    $1 \times 2 = 2$
$3 \times 4 = 12$
$5 \times 6 = 30$
$7 \times 8 = 56$
$9 \times 10 = 90$
$11 \times 12 = 132.$

48. You should check that your friend hasn't boiled his egg, which would make the egg spin for far longer.

49. The answer is FOUR. To see why, suppose the answer was SEVEN. This cannot be correct because this answer has 5 letters, not 7. However, FOUR does have 4 letters and is a valid answer. In fact it is the only number, when spelled out in letters, that has the same amount of letters as the number specifies.

50. SEMESTER.

51. Anything that could be prefixed by "Seventh", so Heaven and Day are acceptable answers. The series goes First Aid, Second Guess, Third Degree, Fourth Estate, etc.

52. One answer is :

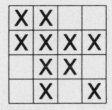

53. Bar magnets are active only at their ends, but act just like ordinary iron bars in the middle. Here, if bar 1 sticks to bar 2 then 2 is a magnet, and vice versa if bars 1 and 2 swap positions.

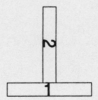

54. UNDERGROUND and ANTIOXIDANT. Notice some letters are used twice.

55. The letters of MONOCHROME are seen.

56. PASTER (the clues give Master, Poster, Patter, Passer, Pastor, Pastes).

57. No. Pythagoras' Theorem says that for a right-angled triangle :

$$x^2 + y^2 = z^2$$

where $z$ is the length of the side opposite the right-angle. For the triangle in the question this means :

$$a^2 + a^2 = b^2$$
$$2a^2 = b^2$$

Taking the square root of both sides :

$$\sqrt{2}a = b$$

Therefore $a$ and $b$ can never both be whole numbers, since the left-hand side is now an irrational number.

58. (a). Like any buoyant object, the balloon will want to oppose the gravitational field ("g-force") felt by the car.

59. The "Eagle" lunar spaceship module which lies in the Sea of Tranquillity on the Moon.

60. The picture of the guitar is incorrect as one of its six strings is missing.

61. They are all words that can be spelt phonetically using one letter : the pictures are a Bee (B), Pea (P), Ewe (U), Jay (J), Tea (T), Eye (I).

62. Father lent them another pound coin so that they had 24 coins. Thus Albert gets £12, Bernard gets £8, Claire gets £3. This leaves one coin left over, which they give back.

63. The probability of a head followed by a tail is equal to that of a tail followed by a head, despite the bias. Therefore toss the coin twice and keep doing so until you get a pair of tosses which are dissimilar. Take the first result of these tosses.

64. Most parachutes NEED a hole in them! If they didn't let some air through, the parachute would swing wildly from side to side.

65. The picture of the dice. This picture shows the 3 and 4 dot sides in the wrong places – they add up to 7 and therefore should be opposite one another.

66. They all make five new words when read backwards – Lamina, Diaper, Reward, Spacer and Snoops.

67. 25 feet. If you imagine unravelling the column you would find it looks like :

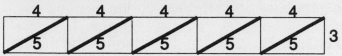

Since 3 squared plus 4 squared equals 5 squared (by Pythagoras' Theorem), and as there are five complete spirals around the column, the answer is 5 x 5 = 25.

68. I am most probably blocking the small hole drilled into the casing of the pen, preventing the pressure from equalizing. Therefore no ink comes out.

69. The items above the line require colour to distinguish between the identical parts.

70. 20 square centimetres. Since the figure can be rearranged into five squares, and since there were four squares to start with, each new square must be 0.8 of an old square. We use 0.8 x 25 = 20.

217

71. MATHEMATICAL. The clues refer to mat-he-ma-ti-cal and lac-it-am-eh-tam.

72. Zero, because the (n−n) term in the middle of the product equals zero; multiplying any numbers by zero equals zero, no matter what the values of the numbers are.

73. Both directions (rocking back and forth, first anticlockwise then clockwise).

74. Suitable answers include : (i) Square manholes can only fit in the hole four ways. Round holes fit any way. (ii) They can be rolled into position. (iii) They use less material than a square manhole of equal width. (iv) They cannot possibly fall through the hole (square manholes can fall through the diagonal). (v) They have no sharp corners.

75. The answer is :

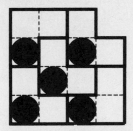

Since the diagram is basically made up of 15 squares, and since each shape has to have one of the five dots, then each piece must be made up of 3 squares. These must either be L-shapes (as shown) or 3-square rods (which doesn't work).

76. W. The letters within the circle, trapezium, triangle and square make up the words Spring, Winter, Summer and Autumn respectively.

77. Xavier, Yves and Zillah should all buy Wilf a drink. This is because Wilf owes one drink but is owed four drinks. Xavier owes two drinks and is owed one drink, so owes a drink. Likewise, Yves and Zillah owe one drink. This gives the answer.

78. Only statement 5 is correct. 1 and 2 are clearly wrong, otherwise pulleys would be pointless. There would be less friction in system A because there are less rubbing surfaces, so A is more energy efficient. Hence 5 is right and 3 is wrong. 4 is incorrect because A requires more force to be applied over a shorter distance.

79. All the items above the line have to be put inside something else to be useful.

80. Thirteen routes. The way to work it out is to calculate the number of ways to arrive at each junction in turn.

81. (one) NIGHT STAND, (two) TIMING, (three) WISE MEN, (four) POSTER BED, (five) SENSES, (six) PACK, (seven) SEAS, (eight) DAY CLOCK, (nine) LIVES, (ten) COMMANDMENTS.

82. $23. Suppose we consider all the possible bets :

$5 chips only cover 0, 5, 10, 15, 20, 25, 30, 35, 40, ...
One $7 chip + $5 chips cover 7, 12, 17, 22, 27, ...
Two $7 chips + $5 chips cover 14, 19, 24, 29, 34, ...
Three $7 chips + $5 chips cover 21, 26, 31, 36, 41, ...
Four $7 chips + $5 chips cover 28, 33, 38, 43, 48, ...
Five $7 chips + $5 chips cover 35, 40, ... again.

So each series covers all the numbers ending in 0/5, 7/2, 4/9, 1/6 or 3/8. But the 3/8 series begins at 28 onwards, so 3, 8, 13, 18, and 23 can't be made. 23 is the largest of these.

83. Only one. By placing two feet on the same level (which can always be done) the third foot is then adjusted until the camera becomes level.

84. YES, because you take the last letters of the acronyms. So VSO is voluntarY servicE overseaS, hence Y, E, S. The other acronyms are AfricaN NationaL CongresS (taking last

letters gives NLS), extrA sensorY perceptioN (AYN), highesT commoN factoR (TNR), and inteR continentaL ballistiC missilE (RLCE).

85. STATEN ISLAND, New York Harbor. Read the arrows in order as if they were the minute hand of a clock at five-minute intervals.

86. Meltdown, signpost, foxglove, offspring, weekday.

87. 4/3, or four thirds. You can work it out by :

$$4a = a + 4$$
$$3a = 4$$

Dividing both sides by 3 :

$$a = \frac{4}{3}$$

88. After 504 seconds, which is the lowest common multiple of 6, 7, 8 and 9.

89. The man could have stabbed himself with an icicle.

90. Pages 16, 25 and 26. Page 16 must be missing because it is on the back of page 15. The supplement must be numbered from 13 to 28, so the sum of the pages on each leaf must add up to (13 + 14 + 27 + 28 =) 82. Likewise 15 + 16 + 25 + 26 = 82.

91. A in a diamond. Reading downwards row-by-row, the like symbols spell out the names of five countries : Egypt, Italy, Kenya, Libya, Yemen.

92. Luckily for Postie Pete, the hole was a catflap measuring 20 by 21 centimetres. The letter can easily be slotted through the diagonal which is 29 cms long :

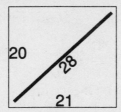

93. (ii), since we use the formula for the area of a circle :

$$\text{Area} = \pi \times (\text{radius})^2$$
$$\text{Area of black tyre} = (\pi \times 5^2) - (\pi \times 4^2)$$
$$= (25 - 16)\pi = 9\pi$$
$$= \pi \times 3^2 = \text{Area of inner hub}$$

94. Everyone jumped in to have a swim but forgot to put a ladder out so that they could get back on the boat.

95. 10 metres also. Imagine the ladder was in the opposite direction. It is a radius of the circle whose radius we know to be 10 metres.

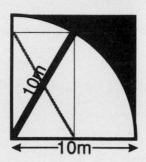

96. When pronounced, the words sound like other words : BOUGH, DOUGH, ROUGH, THROUGH, each of which ends in OUGH.

97. He is probably a shopkeeper or other merchant. 12 + 25% = 16 is correct because it means 12 + (25% of 16) = 16. The 25% addition represents the profit margin on the 12 he wishes to add. If £15 was the selling price, the extra £3 would only give a 20% profit.

98. None – only petrol engines use spark plugs.

99. Add a line to the top of the 10 to give :
        20 TO 5 = 4.40.

100. The Statue of Liberty is back-to-front.

101. Blurb, Fluff, Going, Nylon, Plump (also Pin-up, Polyp, Pop-up, Primp), Widow.

102. 48 points. It takes 4 points to win a game, so to win 2 sets requires 2 x 6 x 4 = 48.

103. Picture 5 cannot be folded up to make a cube.

104. 210, because the series is comprised of the powers of two (1, 2, 4, 8, 16, 32, 64, 128, 256, etc.) grouped into threes.

105. Simply change the corner lines.

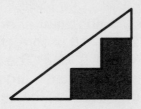

The area of the original triangle was 0.5 x 4 x 3 = 6. Taking away the three shaded squares leaves an area of 3 squares.

106. It is the longest word that can be made using only consonants.

107. 50 feet in diameter, because :

$$r^2 = x^2 + y^2 \text{ for a circle}$$

$$r^2 = (r-5)^2 + (r-10)^2$$

$$0 = r^2 - 30r + 125$$

$$r = \frac{30 \pm \sqrt{900 - 500}}{2} \quad \text{using the formula for a quadratic equation}$$

$$= \frac{30 \pm 20}{2} = 25 \text{ or } 5$$

It can't be 5 since that's too small, so it must be 25 feet in radius; i.e. 50 feet in diameter.

108. 6 revolutions per minute.

$$(\text{A speed}) \times (\text{A teeth}) = (\text{B speed}) \times (\text{B teeth})$$

$$27 \times 8 = 36 \times ?$$

$$? = \frac{27 \times 8}{36} = 6$$

109. Between the 7 and the 2. The order depends on the number of "segments" required to make up the digital number. 7 uses three segments, 2 uses five, and 4 uses four.

110. c3, c5, c7, e3, e7, g3, g5. Adding the knights here protects the (as yet undefended) squares h1, g2, a8, b1, a2, b3, h7, g8 and f7.

111. Skyjack, Buzzsaw, Grapevine, Rendezvous, Headquarters.

112. 51, because 3 + 5 + 7 = 15, digits reversed = 51.

113. He was on a rotating space ship. The coin refuses to spin because it has inertia (and therefore is trying to counteract the gravitational forces on it) but the opposition force is changing all the time because it is on an already spinning space ship.

114. Either E (for zero point fivE) or F (for halF) are correct answers. Likewise, eleveN = 11, hundreD = 100, siX = 6, twentY = 20.

115. It is the Arc de Triomphe in Paris.

116. PUMP, to give Bicycle Pump, Beer Pump, Hand Pump, Water Pump.

117. 17160. There are fifteen possible places to put the black. From the remaining fourteen spaces suppose we number the yellow balls 1 to 7. There are fourteen places to put ball 1, thirteen to put ball 2, and so on until ball 7 is put in any of eight places. Therefore this gives

$$14 \times 13 \times 12 \times 11 \times 10 \times 9 \times 8 = 17,297,280$$

combinations. However, the yellow balls all look the same. There are:

$$7 \times 6 \times 5 \times 4 \times 3 \times 2 \times 1 = 5,040$$

different ways of numbering the balls. (The red balls are already accounted for since they take up the remaining spaces.) Remembering we have to divide by three (since the triangle can be rotated 120 degrees) the answer is :

$$\left(15 \times \frac{14 \times 13 \times 12 \times 11 \times 10 \times 9 \times 8}{7 \times 6 \times 5 \times 4 \times 3 \times 2 \times 1}\right) \div 3 = 17,160$$

118. (b). Both ends are raised, but (because of the different radii of the rotating cylinders) the left-hand side winds up faster than the right-hand side.

119. Sundials always go "clockwise" because of the Earth's rotation around the Sun. Early civilizations used sundials as their first timing devices.

120. 3. The number in each shape represents the number of neighbours the shape has.

# ANSWERS TO LAP 13

121. They are all palindromes (i.e. the words read the same backwards and forwards). The pictures represent Noon, Rotor, Eye, Sexes, Kayak, Radar.

122. £64.78 is not divisible by four, whereas all the components of the total (2780, 32, 88, 12) are.

123. One face and one edge.

124. Atom, Atop and Stow (A to M, A to P, S to W).

125. Add a leaf to squares c1 and e5, a star to a3 and d4, and a circle to b2 and a4.

126. They make up "portmanteau words" :
Breakfast + Lunch = Brunch
Chuckle + Snort = Chortle
Flame + Glare = Flare
Glamorous + Ritz = Glitz
Motor + Hotel = Motel
Smoke + Fog = Smog

127. 951. Each number in the series is found by adding the previous three numbers, so the last figure is 153 + 281 + 517 = 951.

128. Die 3, because the "B" face should be the other way up.

129. A whip. The end of the whip can travel at speeds of up to 700 miles per hour. The "cracking" sound is in fact a miniature sonic boom.

130. The answer is :

The diagrams are the results of two dice, one with black dots, one with white dots, merged together.

131. T, since the letters spell out ROMEO and JULIET alternately.

132. £15,000. If one writes out the information in the form of equations :

$$7 \text{ acres} + \text{profit} = £24,000$$
$$\ominus \ 4 \text{ acres} + \text{profit} = £15,000$$
$$\overline{3 \text{ acres} = £9,000}$$

So 4 acres costs £12,000 and (using the middle equation above) we can see that the profit the estate agent makes is £3,000. We are told this is the same on either deal.

The only way the agent could sell 26 acres is by five deals (three lots of 4 acres, two lots of 7 acres). Making £3,000 on each deal means the total profit is £15,000.

133. CONGENIAL. The chemical symbols for the elements are Co, N, Ge, Ni and Al.

134. Move one line from the equals to the minus (effectively changing the positions of the equals and minus signs). Then turn the book upside down! The equation then reads 569 − 288 = 281, a correct sum.

135. An ellipse/oval shape, as shown here :

136. ANTENNA. Removing the first and last two letters of each word gives the numbers ONE, TWO, EIGHT and NINE.

137. 379. For each box, the number is the total of the boxes to the top, top-left and left.

138. 286 per day. There are twelve reversible times for each hour, except that two has to be subtracted for both AM and PM to stop 12:00 being counted twice. So the answer is :

$$((12 \times 12) - 1) \times 2 = 286$$

139. None – steel is less dense than mercury so the balls will float!

140. The lifeboat. All the other objects have holes, you would hope the lifeboat does not!

141. RESTATE. The other words are Estate, State, Tate, Ate.

142. 27 million. If you think of a six figure mileometer (starting with 000001, 000002, etc.) then in any of the six positions the numbers 0 to 9 appear 100,000 times. Hence : (1+2+3+4+5+6+7+8+9+0) x 100,000 = 4,500,000. Multiplying this by six (for the six digit positions) gives the answer.

143. (c), since copper expands more than platinum, and brass expands more than iron.

144. It is so that 6 and 9 are not confused. If the projectionist looked at these digits on the film it would be possible to get the film the wrong way up.

145. 27 cubes.

146. 5. They are the first positive numbers, when spelled out, to contain the letters of the alphabet : one thousAnd, one Billion, one oCtillion, one hunDreD, onE, Four, eiGht, tHree, so fIve comes next.

[Explanatory note – In the UK the first number is "one hundred And one" (whereas Americans say "one hundred one"), the second number could be 1,000,000,000,000 (a UK billion, although the US version is becoming more popular) and the UK octillion is different.]

147. (a) is the correct answer. It can be rigorously proved, but here are a couple of ways of justifying the answer:

Method 1 :
$\frac{1}{3} + \frac{2}{3} = 1$
But $\frac{1}{3} = 0.3333...$
and $\frac{2}{3} = 0.6666...$
So $0.3333... + 0.6666... = 1$
Hence $0.9999.... = 1$

Method 2 :
Let $\quad\quad x = 0.9999...$
So $\quad\quad 10x = 9.9999...$
Hence $\quad 9x = 9$
$\quad\quad\quad\quad x = 1$
So $0.9999... = 1$

148. A paper cup, or other shape which has a base that has a smaller diameter than its open rim.

149. (b), to form :
MIS "take" NLY = MISTAKENLY.
Likewise, HOB"by"IST, UNS"add"LED, NON"plus"SED, AIM"less"LY.

150. Piece 1 is left over.

**151. ABSOLUTELY.** Split the paragraph up into smaller segments, each of which implies a letter :
Midday = Middle of DAY = A
Starting block = 1st letter of BLOCK = B
Last of the Mohicans = Last letter of MOHICANS = S
Second in Command = 2nd letter in COMMAND = O
and so on.

**152. 1 hour.** If the steaks are numbered 1 to 6, each having sides a and b, then :
10 mins – brown 1a and 2a; 20 mins – brown 1b and 3a
30 mins – brown 2b and 3b; 40 mins – brown 4a and 5a
50 mins – brown 4b and 6a; 60 mins – brown 5b and 6b

**153. 26 cubes.** The worm's journey will take him to white and black cubes alternately. There are 14 white cubes and only 13 black cubes so, since he starts at a white cube, he MUST miss out one white cube before ending up at the middle black cube.

**154.** The correct answer would be "No", because Noah took two of every variety of creature onto the ark. Obviously Noah didn't know that some species (such as snails) are hermaphrodites and are perfectly able to reproduce by themselves.

155. Put X on row 3, Y on row 1, and Z on row 3. The letters on row 1 have vertical symmetry only (that is, their left and right halves are reflections of one another). The letters on row 2 have horizontal symmetry (their top and bottom halves are reflections). Row 3 contains the letters with 180 degree rotational symmetry (turn them upside down and they look the same). The letters on Row 4 have no symmetry at all.

156. It is the SHORTEST English sentence to use all the letters of the alphabet. (There are shorter sentences but they use abbreviations.)

157. $\frac{50}{\pi}$ or about 15.9 metres.
Circumference of a circle $= 2\pi \times$ radius
If the height of the poles is $h$,
and the radius of the Earth is $R$,
then $2\pi(R+h) - 2\pi R = 100$
So $2\pi h = 100$, hence $h = 100 \div 2\pi \approx 15.9$m.

158. (b), since no cogs will move at all! The middle cog is being forced in both directions at once. (N.B. Zero is an even number.)

159. An athlete during the course of a 10,000m race, since her right leg would be on the outside of the track.

160. RETSINA (a type of Greek wine).

161. DEATHBED, since you can prefix these letters before each word. D-Day, A-Bomb, T-Shirt, H-Bomb, B-Movie are well known. An E-Boat is indeed a type of boat. An E-Number is a code given to certain food additives by the European Union. A D-Ring is a common piece of equipment used in parachuting and rock climbing.

162. Only one in 3. There are six possible combinations of the bullets. Of these, you only win if the bullets are in chambers 2, 3 and 4 or in 4, 5 and 6.

163. 96, because it only occurs between the hours 00–05, 10–15 and 20–23, six times per hour.

164. DAVID. (D=500 in Roman numerals, V=5, A=first letter, 1=first number).

165. Seven pieces.

166. There are no Es in the passage. Nor are there any in the remaining 50,000 words of the book, which was published in 1939.

167. 250,500 cms, or 2505m, or 2.505km. Basically, we want the answer to :

$$2 \times (1 + 2 + 3 + \ldots + 499 + 500)$$
$$= 2 \times (250 \times 501)$$

since the number in the bracket is just 250 pairs of 501 (pair together the numbers from either end).

168. Never, because the left pendulum is to the right of its swing at 6, 12, 18, 24, 30... seconds. The right pendulum is to the left of its swing at 5, 15, 25, 35, 45... seconds. Since the first series never ends in 5 but the second series always ends in 5 the pendulums won't touch.

169. Because every March 27th Uncle Brian forgets to put his clock forward an hour at 1am!

170. The answer is shown below :

# ANSWERS TO LAP 18

171. The word MILL, to give Sugar mill, Flour mill, Wool mill, Pepper mill.

172. 5:19pm. From the two pieces of information we deduce that the fraction of the journey that took an hour is :

$$\frac{2}{3}-\frac{1}{4}=\frac{8}{12}-\frac{3}{12}=\frac{5}{12}$$

Therefore the whole journey took :

$$\frac{(12\times60)}{5}=144 \text{ minutes}$$

Now, as a quarter of 144 is 36, he must have set off at 2:55, so he arrived 144 minutes later at 5:19.

173. Roll them – the faster one is solid.

174. These letters look similar whether in lower case or capitals, whereas other letters look different (A and a, for instance).

175. Two times. The outer ball rotates four times, the inner twice.

176. The valid words are : arm, ear, eye, gum, gut, hip, jaw, leg, lip, rib, toe.

177. 2.25.

178. Yes :

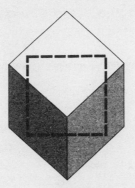

179. Deborah was born in Cambridge, Massachusetts, USA; Katherine was born in Cambridge, England.

180. 25%, or one-in-four. The colours were a clue. Since EACH board has 22 white, 21 grey and 21 black squares, and since each triple domino covers one white, one grey and one black square (no matter where it is) then the uncovered square must be white on BOTH boards. Thus the only ones this could be are the four marked below :

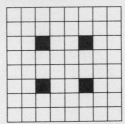

181. STRESSED, which reads DESSERTS backwards.

182. 7, because the sequence goes :

$$1\times1\times1\times1\times1\times1\times1=1$$
$$2\times2\times2\times2\times2\times2=64$$
$$3\times3\times3\times3\times3=243$$
$$4\times4\times4\times4=256$$
$$5\times5\times5=125$$
$$6\times6=36$$
$$7=7$$

183. (a). Since they are of equal mass they will rise at the same speed.

184. By lying along one corner of the square corridor. A 30 foot boulder leaves a 5 foot gap on each side which is comfortably wider than Illinois's shoulders.

185. The picture would be :

The pictures represent the planets of the solar system and their moons. (Notice that Neptune is number nine, because until 1999 it is farther out than Pluto.)

186. EIGHTH, which is an anagram of HEIGHT. All the words in the box have anagrams (eg. VETOED = DEVOTE, GRUDGE = RUGGED, etc.).

187. Here are three possible answers :

$$7 \times 3 + 4 = 5^2$$
$$7 \times 4 = 5^2 + 3$$
$$7 \times 3 = 4^2 + 5$$

188. 44, since it happens twice every hour (giving 48) but there are only three between 2 to 4, and 8 to 10, so 4 has to be subtracted.

189. 8; each number represents the number of letters in each word of the question.

190. Three of the shaded blocks move in the directions shown, so the fourth picture is :

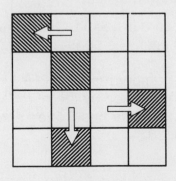

**191.** Anything that rhymes with NINE (such as a MINE, a PINE tree, a bottle of WINE etc.), since the other pictures rhyme with the numbers from one to eight (Gun, Shoe, Tree, etc.)

**192.** The three thousand, four hundred and seventieth, because :

$$(9^3 \times 4) + (9^2 \times 6) + (9 \times 7) + 5 = 3470$$

This is the standard method for working out a number using base 9.

**193. (B).** Using the formula for the area of a circle :

Total volume = no. of pipes $\times \pi \times$ radius$^2$

(A) $1 \times \pi 4^2 = 16\pi$
(B) $2 \times \pi 3^2 = 18\pi$
(C) $3 \times \pi 2^2 = 12\pi$

**194.** He was born in 1340 BC and died in 1322 BC, 18 years later. His name is Tut'ankhamun!

**195. 18.** The number represents the number of straight lines multiplied by the number of areas. The final figure has 6 lines and 3 areas, hence 6 x 3 = 18.

196. They are words that contain a Q that is NOT followed by U, namely Aqaba, Iraqi, Qadaffi, Qadi, Qantas, Qatar, Qintar, Qoph.

197. 0.8571429. They are the results shown on a calculator display for the following fractions :

$$\frac{1}{2}, \frac{2}{3}, \frac{3}{4}, \frac{4}{5}, \frac{5}{6}, \frac{6}{7}.$$

198. The cylinder – clearly the sphere or cone can fit into the cylinder so this must be largest.

199. It is an anagram of THE MAMMOTH BOOK OF BRAINSTORMING PUZZLES.

200. Four. The three dimensional solid that has vertices all equidistant from one another is the triangle-based pyramid. If you imagine this inscribed inside a ball, the four points touching the ball indicate the positions for the bases.

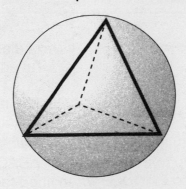

201. The longest I found were 5 letters long (including FLASK, FLASH, FLAGS) although there may be more obscure words depending on which dictionary you use.

202. Vicky does. In the second race, they meet at 10 metres from the finish line, so (as Vicky is the faster runner) she then gains a small lead before taking the tape.

203. It's an easy piece of geometry. The cards are slightly trapezium-shaped (see diagram). When the victim examines her card, Andrew turns the pack around. When Sylvia puts the card back in the pack, Andrew's fingers will automatically lift the card out of the pack.

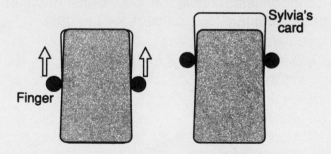

Sylvia's card

Finger

204. "BDC" is the odd one out – the other pieces pair up to form the words ABACUS, GERMAN and CANDLE when fitted together.

205. Here's how we did it, though there are lots of possible ways :

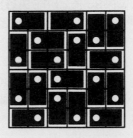

206. DODECAGON, meaning a twelve-sided shape.

207. One way is : top number 7; second row 3, then 1, then 4; third row 5 then 8 then 6; bottom number 2.

208. When water boils, it stays exactly at boiling point forever until all the water has boiled away into steam. So, the Professor should make his coffee now while there still is water in the kettle.

209. Moses! (Geddit? – he took the two stone tablets containing the Ten Commandments from Mount Sinai.)

210. ABRACADABRA.

211. The unclued word is SOLVED. The answers are : Across – 2) Yes, 4) Nap, 6) Slur, 8) Umber, 12) Niece, 13) Cake, 14) Lop, 15) Nee; Down – 1) Census, 3) Salmon, 5) Public, 7) Reveal, 9) Reckon, 11) Deepen.

212. Top row : 1 + 7 / 2; middle row : 6 x 5 – 8; bottom row 4 x 9 – 3.

213. 5 scratches in total, since diamond scratches all three tiles, quartz scratches copper and gypsum, and talc is the softest so doesn't scratch anything.

214. Italy drives on the right-hand side of the road, so should be placed on the right of the line.

215. Since the total of the numbers is 32, and two lines crossing makes four sections, then each partition contains a total of 8.

216. The final answer is GERMAN MANGER. The answers to the individual clues are : 1) EMIT time, 2) SNUG gnus, 3) LEMON melon, 4) Norse SENOR, 5) SWORE worse,

6) SPORADIC Picadors. The words in capitals are the ones you should have put into the grid.

217. A, because this makes all the rows and columns add up to 20.

218. Birds can't swallow food or water without gravity. Humans can swallow when doing handstands since we have muscles that contract to force things down, but birds don't have this ability.

219. A native French speaker who can touch-type. The culprit killed Jack in the dark, then touch-typed a message onto the screen. However, the French use the AZERTY keyboard (shown below) whereas Jack was using the standard QWERTY keyboard.

220. The riddle reads "What has no wings, no rotors and yet can fly?" Turn the book 90 degrees, look at what you have traced and the answer becomes obvious!

221. The words are WATT, ZONED, TUNNEL, ZEPHYR and WOUNDED.

222. Square the number then take away twice the original number. In equation form :

$$Output = Input^2 - (2 \times Input)$$

223. B – it's not as hard as it looks. Move the black dot through the maze-like structure until it's outside. Only in B does the dot come out between the arrows.

224. Canada is 4, since there are four geometric shapes on its national flag, two red rectangles, a white rectangle and the maple leaf. So, for example, this explains why the USA is 64 (50 stars, the blue rectangle which contains the stars, and 13 stripes).

225. Across – ITS, CADET, ARENA, READY, AS; Down – CAR, AREA, IDEAS, TEND, STAY.

226. I boasted that I could form the word BIGHEAD.

227. 10 (representing X). The common Roman numerals have been put into alphabetical order – C, D, I, L, M, V, X.

228. The words SQUARE NUMBER can be read after just two twists of the cube :

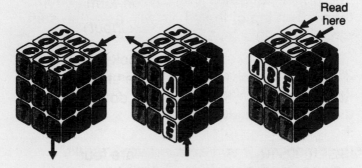

Read here

229. The man had been doing nothing wrong by burning pieces of meaningless cloth. However, he happened to be in Libya, where the national flag is a plain green rectangle. By burning it he had offended the crowd and broken the law.

230. A picture of an angel.

231. The anagram is DIAGRAM.
Across – 1) Stem, 5) Tide, 6) Alga, 7) Reed;
Down – 1) Star, 2) Tile, 3) Edge, 4) Mead.

232. Place "b" down first, then put "a" on top,
then "c" on top of that. This will make the sum
read : 33 x 29 = 297 + 660 = 957.

233. The reason is due to the peculiarities of
the hour hand. You can always tell where 12
o'clock is by noting the only place where both
the hour and minute hand point to the same
hour marking. If you accidentally mistake 3
o'clock for 12 o'clock, the hands would not
align properly.

234. This is a lateral thinking question for a
good reason. If you use Roman numerals (with
C in the circles, X in the diamonds, and I in the
triangles) everything becomes clear...

235. The answer relies on counting the black
(as well as white) sections.

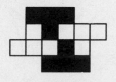

236. ATMOSPHERIC can be spelt out.

237. The record has several interleaved grooves. The diagram shows one track, the others are similar spirals using the gaps.

238. A and B fit together if one of them is turned upside-down. If you thought A and C fit together, the block marked here prevents this.

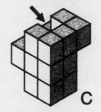

239. It reads "Congratulations, you have solved it". You probably got the answer by looking at alternate letters, but this code was traditionally read by winding the paper strip around a pole. Try it for yourself!

240. I reckon you need to move 8 mirrors (in black). Notice the use of both sides of one mirror near the bottom of the course. The fact that the path crosses doesn't matter either, since laser light does not interfere with itself when crossing.

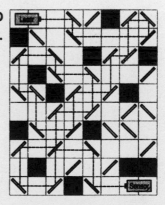

241. Across – 4) Bauxite, 6) Ace, 7) Oatmeal, 9) Lei, 10) Granite; Down – 1) Cavalry, 2) Examine, 3) Stealth, 5) Ice, 8) Tea.

242. The fence posts will have to be next to each other! In this situation the six-foot long chain is only one foot from the ground.

243. There is a circle, radius $10 + \frac{5}{\pi}$ miles from the South Pole, which satisfies the condition, as you will see from the diagram. (In fact, depending on how many times you circle the pole, there are other answers.)

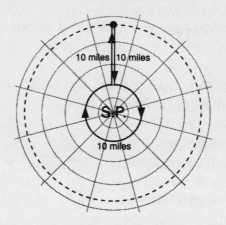

244. Ten months became twelve in honour of Augustus and Julius Caesar in 44 BC.

245. The answer is 42. Hands up all those who thought the answer was 44 (=396 ÷ 9). If so, you overlooked the fact that after the 42nd square you are left with a useless 1 x 18 inch strip.

246. The newspaper headline is a palindrome (that is, it can be read backwards and forwards as the same thing).

247. The full list is infinitely long, but the pattern starts 1 and 0, 2 and –1, 3 and –2, 4 and –3, 5 and –4, 6 and -5, and so on. The mathematical way to solve the problem is :

$$x^2 - x = y^2 - y$$
$$x(x-1) = y(y-1)$$

Therefore $x = 1 - y$
or $x = 0$, $y = 0$ (not allowed)

so $x = 1 - y$ is the formula to use.

248. It will be 4.5 units long. This is because the springs are normally 1.5 units long, and the weight stretches them by one unit. However, the combination of springs in the diagram makes the extension 1.5 times longer. Hence the answer is 3 + (1.5 x 1) = 4.5 units.

249. A ghost train or other theme-park ride.

250. 46 (28 edges plus 18 faces.)

# PROGRESS CHART

Plot your scores on the chart and see if you are
keeping up with the target to beat.

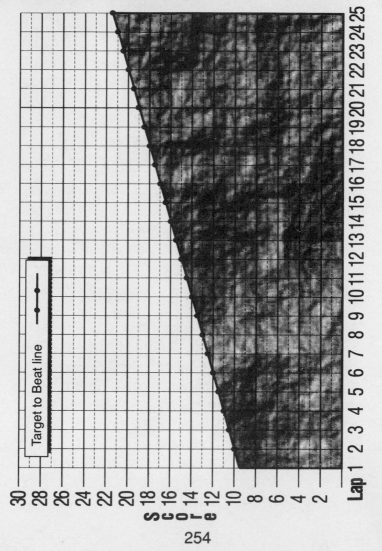